MATHEMATICS FOR PARENTS

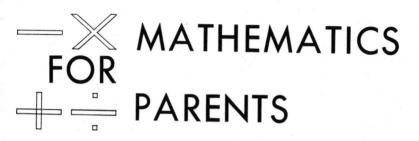

MATHEMATICS FOR PARENTS

CARL B. ALLENDOERFER

PROFESSOR OF MATHEMATICS

UNIVERSITY OF WASHINGTON

THE MACMILLAN COMPANY, NEW YORK   COLLIER-MACMILLAN LIMITED, LONDON

Third Printing 1965

Preliminary edition © Carl B. Allendoerfer, 1963

Library of Congress catalog card number: 65-12006

THE MACMILLAN COMPANY, NEW YORK
COLLIER-MACMILLAN CANADA, LTD., TORONTO, ONTARIO

PRINTED IN THE UNITED STATES OF AMERICA

PREFACE

This book has been written to answer the many questions about the "new mathematics" which come to me as I move about in public. When I have lunch in the Faculty Club my colleagues ask me about this "base 7" business their children are being exposed to; when I meet someone at a summer resort he is likely to turn out to be a member of a school board who wants the real truth about SMSG; and when I go out in the evening my friends blame me for all the troubles their children are having in school with mathematics that even father never saw before. Although I am a mathematician by profession, I sometimes like to talk about other things. So this little volume is meant to get me off the hook, for hereafter when I see a mathematical gleam in the eye of an approaching parent I can say: "I know what you are about to ask. I have it all written up in my new book." And with a reference to my publishers, I shall turn on my heel and look for some nonmathematical nonparent who is still willing to talk about the Yankees, taxes, the weather, or the Russians.

The book is really divided into two parts. The first four chapters describe the nature of the current revolution in mathematics and make suggestions for parents who are interested in the best mathematical education of their children. Very little technical mathematics appears in these chapters, and they should be understandable to even dear old dad who had trouble with algebra in the ninth grade. If, however, you have more fortitude and actually want to see the details, the last nine chapters are for you. Here I have written an easygoing account of some of the most important technical changes that have occurred recently. When you have read through these, you should at a minimum recognize the words your children are using when they talk about their school mathematics. You may even be able to break the barrier and help them with their homework, but for most of you this will require more study. If you wish to go beyond this book, I strongly recommend my elementary text *Principles of Mathematics* (jointly written with C. O. Oakley, 2nd ed., McGraw-Hill, New York, 1963) which seems to be within the grasp of many of the current generation of high school students.

Good luck!

Acknowledgments. My thanks are due to KCTS-TV, the educational television station for Seattle and King County, Washington, who made it possible for me to deliver a preliminary version of this material as a series of television broadcasts. Some of the chapters were also delivered as lectures before the Monday Club of Seattle, the Mathematical Association of America, and various groups in Hawaii and Australia where I was a visiting lecturer. My thanks to these audiences whose questions have led to many improvements in the presentation.

Carl B. Allendoerfer

Seattle, Washington

TABLE OF CONTENTS

CHAPTER 1 THE NATURE OF MATHEMATICS

Before you can make sense of the current recommendations for the reform of mathematics teaching, you must have an understanding of the nature of mathematics. To many of you mathematics probably means ordinary arithmetic with its set rules for computation. Others may remember algebra as a collection of special procedures which, by some sort of magic, can be used to get the answer in the book. And geometry is a mysterious subject full of theorems to memorize and outrageous tricks by means of which we prove the truth of perfectly obvious relationships in nature. It is no wonder that parents ask me, "How can there be anything new in mathematics? Are the old formulas not still true?" So that you can fit your present recollection of mathematics into the whole picture as a mathematician sees it, I shall begin with a description of the nature of our subject. Later we shall discuss the details of its separate branches.

Let me begin by describing the structure of a mathematical theory in a mature form. In other words, let me show you how a piece of mathematics looks when it has been completed and polished and written up (or is it "embalmed"?) in textbooks. As we shall see, this picture is quite different from that of a mathematical theory in the process of development.

I begin our story with "nature", a word which I wish to use in the broadest possible sense (see Fig. 1). Under this heading I shall include all physical and biological aspects of nature as well as human disciplines such as economics, psychology, anthropology, business, and warfare. The scholars in these various fields have initially gone to very great trouble to describe their subjects as best they can in words, and as their scholarship matures they begin to investigate

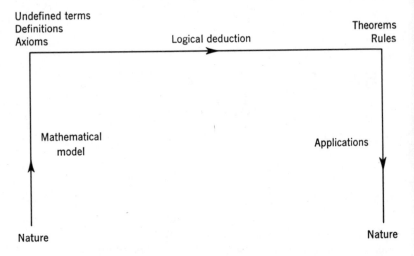

Fig. 1. Structure of mathematics—polished version.

the quantitative aspects of their domains. Then they join with mathematicians to build what is currently called a *mathematical model* of their portion of nature. This model is incomplete in many ways, for first it contains only the quantitative and geometric aspects of nature, and, moreover, like all models it is only an imperfect copy and not the real thing. Extant models differ in their degree of excellence; they are remarkably exact for the physical sciences, but are just emerging in hesitant form in the social sciences. But whatever the value of the model, it is the beginning of a mathematical theory.

Let us examine the character of such a model. In the first place, it is necessary to settle upon a technical vocabulary to describe the observed phenomena. It is surprising to most nonmathematicians to be told that the basic words in this vocabulary cannot be defined. In order to appreciate this point, consider the plight of an American who tries to read a French text with only the aid of a French language dictionary. He can look up each word, but finds that the definitions are in terms of other French words which have no meaning for him. The case is hopeless unless in some other fashion he learns the meaning of a basic collection of French words. In mathematics we have no way of assigning meanings to this basic collection of technical words, and must leave them undefined. Thus in geometry the words *point, line,* and *plane,* are taken as undefined. I agree that we may well have mental pictures of what these words connote, but this is quite another matter from giving them satisfactory definitions. The rest of the technical vocabulary is built up from these words by the familiar process of definition.

Next we wish to use these words to say something about our observations of nature, and so we form sentences which we believe to be true. Actually sentences such as "Two points determine a straight line" cannot be shown to be true by any form of reasoning, for how can one establish the truth of a sentence containing two words which are not defined? This sentence is in fact an abstraction from the observation that there is a unique straight road between a pair of towns, and thus it is part of our model of nature. Sentences of this kind which describe basic observed facts of nature are called *axioms* and by assumption they are *true.*

Our model, then, consists of a collection of abstractions: undefined words, words defined in terms of these, and statements called axioms which are assumed to be true. The construction of such a model is a creative act of the highest order. In many ways it compares with the landscape of the artist or the novel of the writer, each of whom is expressing in his own way aspects of nature which appear important to him at the time. Let us examine a few models of this kind.

The first illustration of a mathematical model that a child meets is that of the concept of *number.* In his early years he learns to count and is able to understand phrases such as: "three blocks", "three trees", "three boys", and the like. But what does "three" mean all by itself? Primitive tribes have difficulty answering this question, and some of them use different words for "three" when they are counting different kinds of objects. As a matter of fact there is a

trace of this in our own language, for we use different words to
describe groups of various kinds of animals, such as: *flock* of sheep,
herd of cattle, *pack* of wolves, or *covey* of quail. There is no need for
all these separate names for the idea involved, and you can see the
confusion that would result if we extended this practice to our ordinary counting operations.

But what is "three"? It is an abstraction derived from our experience in actual counting. When we abstract the other counting
numbers and formulate the rules for computing with these, we have
constructed the mathematical model which we call *arithmetic*. The
troubles which young children have in arithmetic have their origin
in this process of abstraction, for this is the first time the youngsters
have met anything abstract. Now that we understand the nature of
the difficulties, we can consider what needs to be done to help the
children over this hurdle.

Another illustration of a mathematical model is the usual formulation of plane geometry. As you will remember, geometry begins
logically with a set of axioms, or postulates, and a set of undefined
terms. These are obtained by abstraction from the physical process
of measuring parcels of land. A farmer's field has corners, boundaries,
and the land area itself. The corners may be marked with posts and
the boundaries with fences which are only approximately straight.
In our model these posts become points, the fences become lines, and
the field itself becomes a plane. Point, line, and plane are our abstractions. Now we look at the field and observe, for instance, that
there is a single fence between every pair of corner posts. In our
abstraction this becomes the axiom: there is a unique line passing
through any pair of distinct points. By this process we build up the
model which we use as our foundation of plane geometry.

A further example of the construction of a model is Newton's
invention of the calculus. His concern was with an appropriate
theory to explain the observed motions of the planets in our solar
system. Quantitative measurements and elementary mathematical
descriptions of the planetary orbits were at hand, but there was no
systematic theory which accounted for them. Newton's first task
was to develop an adequate vocabulary which included the definitions of words such as *velocity* and *acceleration*. These definitions are
now the basic ideas of the differential calculus. He did not lay a solid

foundation of undefined terms and axioms, and these had to be supplied at a later date. Like all model builders, he painted with a broad brush and left the details to be filled in by lesser men. Nevertheless, he did state the most essential axioms, which are currently known as Newton's laws of motion. On this foundation he built his theory of gravity and planetary motion. One of Einstein's great contributions is the construction of a different model for this same portion of nature.

A most exciting development at the present time is the construction of similar models in the social and biological sciences. Although these models are far from ideal, they are bold attempts to put these subjects on a firm mathematical foundation and are the forerunners of great things to come.

Once the model is constructed, the mathematician proceeds to prove theorems. These are statements about his subject which can be deduced logically from his assumed axioms. To say that a mathematical statement is *true* is to mean that this statement is a logical consequence of a set of axioms, and nothing more. The notion of absolute truth is entirely foreign to mathematics in spite of the worship of mathematics by laymen who are seeking something that is unchangeable and eternal. If mathematicians were to apply the method of reasoning of their own subject to their personal philosophy of ethics and values, they would be (and frequently are) pure relativists.

The chain is now closed by the applied mathematician who takes the general theorems so deduced, puts numbers in them, and attempts to discover new relationships in nature. Of course, he can prove nothing about nature in this way. Nevertheless, he can arrive at statements about nature which can probably be verified by observation of nature if his original model is reasonably good. Of course, his objective is to find new facts about nature which had not been previously observed, or better, to predict what would be found if a certain measurement or observation were to be made.

I fear that I have misled you into believing that a mathematical theory is built by following these three steps in order; nothing could be farther from the truth. Mathematicians often perform the magical feat of building the fifth storey without first establishing a foundation or even thinking about the first four stories. We start at both ends and the middle and only after decades of effort bring forth the beautiful, logical, and polished gems which we dangle before our students.

More often we follow a different path. Beginning with nature as before, we seek to find as many relationships within it as we can. If we can systematize these we do so, but a lack of organization of our material does not keep us from pushing forward. On the basis of what we have observed, we *guess* theorems and use these to derive other theorems. Immediately we rush to apply these back again to nature and proceed headlong if our predictions are successful. Axioms, logic, and rigor are thrown to the winds, and we become intoxicated with our success and open to dreadful errors.

This process is called *intuition,* and its nature is in no way understood. Several great mathematicians have written accounts of their experiences in this phase of mathematical discovery, but the psychologists are baffled by their testimony. The successful unraveling of this process should be a major contribution to the understanding of the human mind. But explained or not, it is by this means that the great majority of mathematical theorems are first discovered. One of my teachers in graduate school was good for about one hundred such discoveries a week, with an average of only about one which stood up under careful analysis. Yet those that were correct made him one of the great mathematicians of the past generation.

The procedure is then as in Fig. 2. By means of intuition we guess theorems, test them against applications, organize those that survive, find axioms on the basis of which they can be proved and thus build our mathematical model. A little-known trade secret is that in this process theorems come first and axioms second. A good example of this is the re-examination of Euclidean geometry in the past century. It was discovered that many of Euclid's theorems could not be proved from his axioms. Yet we all believed these theorems to be true, and a number of different systems of axioms were developed which had these theorems as their consequences. This process of justifying a belief by trying to find premises from which it can be deduced is shockingly similar to much reasoning in our daily lives, and I am embarrassed to have to let you know that mathematicians are experts at this art.

After the model has been constructed in this way we then prove theorems by deduction and finally seek for applications to nature.

There are, then, four key words in the process of constructing a mathematical theory:

Intuition
Organization
Deduction
Application

We shall see that this same pattern applies to the learning of mathematics, and that any good course in our subject must include all four of these features.

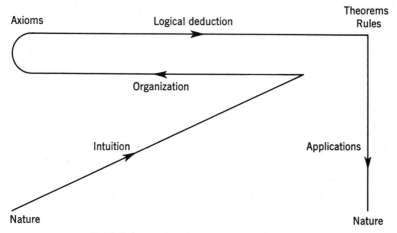

Fig. 2. Structure of mathematics—as it is discovered.

This description of mathematics would have seemed reasonably accurate until something more than one hundred years ago, but it omits the most significant development in our subject during the past century. The breakthrough which stimulated this new point of view was the construction of non-Euclidean geometry. One of Euclid's axioms stated that there exists a unique line through a given point which is parallel to a given line which does not pass through this point (Fig. 3). This axiom was never fully accepted by mathematicians on the ground that it did not have the "self-evident" quality of Euclid's other axioms, and many attempts were made to prove it on the basis of the other axioms. Although no such proofs were obtained, everyone believed that this axiom was true, and in fact Euclidean geometry was given the aura of absolute truth commonly associated with the Bible.

In the early part of the nineteenth century attempts were made to prove this axiom by the method of contradiction. In conformity with this method mathematicians assumed that the axiom was false and hoped to deduce conclusions which contradicted at least one of the remaining axioms. In particular the two alternative axioms were investigated: (1) there is no such parallel, and (2) there are at least two such parallels. Although these mathematicians worked diligently and imaginatively, they were frustrated in that they found no such contradictions. It is reported that Gauss was the first to have arrived at this awkward impasse and that he considered the possibility that

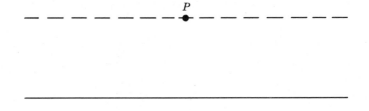

Fig. 3. Euclid's parallel axiom.

alternatives to the parallel axiom were logically possible. So great was the authority of Euclid that he felt it unwise to publish his findings. Later others such as Lobachevski and Bolyai came to similar conclusions, and gradually the secret was shared with the community of mathematicians. The astounding conclusion was that there are three equally acceptable geometries which appear to be satisfactory models of nature. Even today there are no compelling reasons for choosing among them.

It required another fifty years for the major impact of this discovery to transform the character of mathematics, but now we are so deeply imbued with the new spirit that young mathematicians cannot understand why anyone ever thought differently. The new philosophy is that abstract systems of undefined words, axioms, etc. (which we previously called mathematical models), need have nothing whatever to do with nature. They are no longer models of anything, but are merely structures built by mathematicians because they are thought to be worth investigating. Since these abstract mathematical systems did not spring from nature, there is no obligation for their advocates to apply the related theorems back to nature, and consequently we have a mathematics which exists purely of and for itself. A large part of contemporary mathematics is of this kind.

You may wonder how one goes about thinking of such an abstract system, and the process is as difficult to describe as are most creative acts. At the initial stages the abstract systems may be called *mutations* of earlier models of nature. For example, geometry has been extended from three dimensions to an arbitrarily large finite number of dimensions, and finally to an infinite number of dimensions. In algebra we are accustomed to assume that $3 \times 4 = 4 \times 3$ and more generally that $a \times b = b \times a$. In one of the newer algebras the rule is that $a \times b = -b \times a$. Abstract spaces are considered in which the notion of distance between two points has been replaced by a much more general concept of *nearness*. And so on. At each step the new abstraction becomes so familiar to the mathematician that he regards it as concrete and makes it serve as the basis for further abstractions. The length of a mathematical generation is about ten years, and each generation regards with dismay the attitude of the following generation, which treats the marvelous abstractions of their predecessors as trivial or narrow.

Another source of abstraction is the unification of two older theories into a single more general one. The two theories may well have sprung from two different mathematical models of nature without any regard for each other. Their combination into a single abstract theory often illuminates each of the parent theories, and always produces a great economy of thought. The growth of mathematical knowledge is so rapid that without such amalgamations no one could find his way through the morass.

Although the appearance of these modern theories suggests that they have no connection at all with nature, I cannot think of a single one which does not owe its existence to a remote mathematical model of nature out of which it has grown by the processes of mutation and generalization. Perhaps the invention of a theory with no remote roots in nature is beyond the powers of the mind, but more probably such a construction will occur before long as the next major breakthrough in the development of mathematics.

CHAPTER 2 HOW THINGS ARE CHANGING

Let us return to Fig. 1 of the first chapter and look at it in the light of the traditional curriculum in mathematics. Most of you will find that your experience with mathematics was confined to the right side of the figure. You were shown a set of rules and given practice in applying these to a variety of more or less artificial situations. Only rarely (especially in geometry) were you given any idea of the reasons behind the rules or of how you might have invented them yourself. An extreme version of a traditional mathematics textbook might well look like that of Fig. 4.

On the left hand page we have a rule, usually printed in color, and often imperfectly stated. Under this are several worked examples illustrating the application of the rule. On the opposite right hand page there are fifty or one hundred problems to which the rule is to be applied. The student memorizes the rule, works a selection of the problems, and then turns the page. There he finds exactly the same thing, although with a different rule. Consecutive rules may have some relationship, but this is infrequently explained in detail. After a series of some five or ten episodes of this kind, the student is tested on his proficiency, and then proceeds to more rules. All too often the earlier procedures are forgotten, and mathematics appears to the youngster as a collection of rather stupid, isolated tricks which he is supposed to learn by rote.

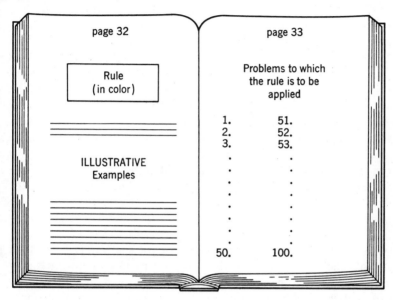

Fig. 4. Traditional textbook.

Teaching with Understanding

The first major change of the current mathematical revolution is to put emphasis on *teaching with understanding* in place of *rote learning*. Of course good teachers have done this all along, but too frequently the teacher himself did not have the necessary background, and all that he could do was to drive his pupils through the book. Teaching with understanding involves presenting the subject as a whole, preferably following the sequence in Fig. 2, so that all four steps are included: intuition, organization, deduction, application.

First we must build intuition. This is accomplished by showing the student a large number of elementary illustrations of the idea which is to be presented later in a formal fashion. From these he gains a feeling for correct procedure, even though he cannot explain it in any precise way. Then the teacher capitalizes on this intuition, and helps the student organize his knowledge. Eventually axioms are introduced and theorems are proved, thus filling in the portions of Fig. 2 which were previously left out. It is most important that the applications be introduced, and that mathematical skills be developed and maintained by periodic review. There is good evidence that *students taught in this fashion learn mathematics more easily and remember it longer* than if they were taught in the rote memory tradition.

To implement this method of teaching, schools are making changes in their curricula. For example, instruction in arithmetic takes into account the laws of algebra which are to come later. If you look ahead to Chapters 7 and 8 you will see that we base algebra on the commutative, associative, and distributive laws. Since these apply equally well to arithmetic, we introduce them intuitively in the elementary school, where they become a natural part of the child's knowledge. Then he has little difficulty with algebra when he meets it in high school. In the same way schools are teaching the facts of plane and solid geometry in the elementary school and in junior high school. The youngsters learn these by constructing figures with ruler and compass, and thus develop their mechanical coordination simultaneously with their mathematical knowledge. Then they are prepared to organize this geometrical knowledge when demonstrative geometry is presented to them as an axiomatic system in the tenth grade. The intuitive aspects of calculus are frequently taught in the twelfth grade to build a foundation for the serious calculus the students will meet in college.

Old and New Topics

Another of the changes in mathematics teaching is the elimination of certain older topics and their replacement with others. There is nothing very dramatic about this, for changes of this kind have been carried on continuously for centuries. These changes, of course, should be gradual and not subject to whims or fads. Let me give a number of illustrations.

In my library I have an arithmetic book, published in 1808, which carries the endorsements of the presidents of Dartmouth, Harvard, and Yale universities. In this text the students studied pounds, shillings, and pence—for we had only recently adopted the decimal system in our currency. They were taught, for instance, to find one-third of 4 pounds, 12 shillings, and 5 pence. Later in the course they were taught not only how to take square root but also cube root, fourth root, and fifth root. These topics have fortunately disappeared from modern arithmetics, but undoubtedly there were head shakers among the old-timers when these changes were made.

The most important trends of this kind at present have to do with the techniques of computation and with solid geometry. Until the 1920's there were only two available methods for accurate computation: longhand and logarithms. Early forms of the desk calculator were available, but these were not in widespread use; and some forward-looking engineers were using slide rules. But most people had to rely on pencils or logarithm tables for their work. Mathematical instruction was geared for this, and students were taught appropriate methods for handling their problems by these means.

Since then we have seen the widespread use of the desk calculator in business and technology, and the universal adoption of the slide rule for approximate calculations by scientists and engineers. Moreover, we are now in the midst of a major new development resulting from the invention of the high-speed electronic computing machine. Methods of handling problems which were designed for efficient hand or logarithmic calculation are now replaced with those which are most appropriate for the use of modern computing equipment. For instance, the old, long method of taking square roots and the logarithmic solution of triangles (in trigonometry) are now obsolete. There is no reason to teach such things to our children just because they were essential tools for our own parents.

The situation concerning solid geometry is somewhat different. This course used to require a semester, usually in the twelfth grade. The purpose was twofold: (1) to reteach the axiomatic method previously taught in the tenth grade, and (2) to train the students in three-dimensional perception. The first of these objectives can now be met in other ways, particularly through the use of axioms in algebra. Perception of relationships in space remains an important objective in the total educational picture, but it is important that it be taught at a much earlier age. For these reasons the formal course in solid geometry has largely disappeared. Some schools have missed the point about space perception and have failed to reintroduce it in other places—this is a most serious mistake. Three-dimensional ideas can be taught to the youngest of children in the early grades, intuitive space geometry can be presented in the junior high, and the ideas of solid geometry (without all their proofs) can be taught hand in hand with the parallel ideas of plane geometry in the tenth grade.

Something like a semester can be saved (for nonaccelerated students) by these omissions, and a number of recommendations are available for filling this time. I am specifically thinking of the last semester of the twelfth grade. By all odds the most attractive subject here, for me, is that of analytic geometry. This beautiful and practical piece of mathematics is absolutely essential for the applications of mathematics to science and for the study of the calculus. It used to be a standard college course, but the colleges, in their haste to teach calculus to all freshmen (ready or not), have drastically shortened the time spent on analytic geometry. This unfortunate development has made mathematical cripples of many of our young engineers and scientists. An excellent scheme for remedying this omission and for giving an exciting last course in high school is to make this course one in analytic geometry.

Another popular suggestion is that this semester be spent on probability with some application to statistics. One cannot escape the applications of probability in any walk of life, for they are with us at the race track, in public opinion polls, in industrial quality control, in all our economic data collection, and in many modern forms of decision making. The suggestion, then, is that students should start the study of probability as early in their lives as possible. A very real problem with such a course, however, is the availability of properly trained teachers. Probability is a special kind of mathematics to which many good mathematicians have never been exposed. Moreover, it can be best taught only by someone who has got his hands dirty by using it in the field. Unless your school has a teacher with these qualifications, it would be wise to discard this as a possible twelfth grade course.

Principals and superintendents are especially fond of introducing calculus into the twelfth grade, for they take pride in this as a sign of their progressive leadership. For unaccelerated students the introduction of much calculus is a bad mistake. I do favor a month or two of intuitive calculus for reasons mentioned above, but any more is likely to replace other essential parts of algebra, trigonometry, or analytic geometry and hence leave the students unprepared for their college work. My message to you as parents is: "Look most critically at your school if it teaches more than eight weeks of calculus to unaccelerated students."

New Language

To many parents the most noticeable sign of change in mathematical education is the use of unfamiliar language. Your children will tell you about *sets* and *open sentences*. They will read -4 as "negative four" instead of "minus four", and they will refer to the commutative, associative, and distributive laws which I mentioned before. Do not be dismayed by this language. I will explain it all to you in later chapters. It is really quite simple, and is very helpful. Although there are extreme mathematical revolutionaries who would like to change the whole vocabulary, most teachers have made only those changes which are essential for precise statements of mathematical ideas. The old language had so many sources of ambiguity that students had to learn the subject by osmosis rather than in a logical way.

Acceleration

Finally I should say something about acceleration. Since all children do not learn with equal speed, the schools have recently been separating the rapid learners from the others and "accelerating" their progress. It is certainly true that some eighth graders are ready for algebra, and that it is a crime to waste a year of their lives giving them more arithmetic when they know it already. Various forms and degrees of acceleration are possible, and each school must adapt its system to meet local conditions. Parents and teachers should remember, however, that the purpose of acceleration is to teach *more* mathematics in the *same* number of years, rather than to enable the students to drop their mathematics before they have finished high school. As I shall develop in greater detail in Chapter 4, mathematical education should be continuous from the first grade into college. Acceleration which leads to fallow years with no course in mathematics does more harm than good.

If your school is introducing an accelerated program, be sure that plans have been made for the continuous study of mathematics through the twelfth grade for accelerated students. The normal twelfth grade course for accelerated students is a serious course in calculus at the college level. But students should not enter such a course unless: (1) they have completed the full curriculum of college preparatory mathematics including analytic geometry, and (2) the school has a teacher who is as well equipped to handle the course as a college professor. Students completing such a course should be well prepared to attack the Advanced Placement Examination of the College Entrance Examination Board. College credit is usually given to those who obtain satisfactory scores on this examination.

The People Involved

I am often asked "Just who is behind all these changes?" There seems to be a fear that they are another manifestation of progressive education or some kind of nostrum sponsored by departments of education. Nothing could be farther from the truth. These changes are the outcome of the joint thinking of a very large number of the nation's best university mathematicians and secondary school teachers. Recently elementary teachers have been taking part in planning the changes in the grade schools. Let me say a few words about how this all came about.

In the early years of this century there was relatively little advanced mathematical competence in the United States. A few universities had professors of outstanding quality, but an ambitious young man was well advised to go to Europe for his advanced training if he planned to be a research mathematician. The teaching of mathematics at the school and college level was apparently satisfactory for the standards of the times, and some textbooks were written that are better than many of their more recent counterparts. About the time of World War I a conscious decision was made to allow the small number of research mathematicians to put their energy into the discovery of new theorems and the training of Ph.D.'s, and to leave the problems of school and undergraduate mathematics to others. This policy was highly successful on the research side, for in less than forty years American mathematics vaulted to a leading position in the world. At the same time school mathematics suffered a serious decline for lack of contact with the exciting changes in the world of mathematical discovery.

The gap between school and research mathematics had become a scandal in the 1930's, and a reform movement was under way when World War II snuffed it out. Because of the strains of the war and the GI bulge, nothing further was accomplished until about 1950. At that time several individual mathematicians began trying out new materials on their college freshmen. Some of these efforts appeared as books, and schoolmen began to take notice. The College Entrance Examination Board appointed its Commission on Mathematics in 1954, and work began in earnest. This commission included both school and college teachers of mathematics, and its formation is a historic event in that these groups had not met together under proper auspices for at least 40 years. The commission's final report was not issued until 1959, but preliminary drafts had been widely circulated in previous years. The plan for reform was ready; all that was needed was the money to support it. To our very great good fortune the Russians launched Sputnik I in 1957, and the public demanded action.

In response to this demand the School Mathematics Study Group (SMSG) was established on the recommendation of the presidents of the American Mathematical Society and the Mathematical Association of America. Generous financial support was provided by the National Science Foundation, and the movement was launched in a big way. SMSG established writing groups composed of university and school mathematicians and has published a "five-foot shelf" of experimental textbooks for elementary and secondary school use.

Private foundations have also financed university writing teams of which I shall only mention that at the University of Illinois. These teams have also published experimental textbooks, and now schools are able to choose among several alternative modern presentations of mathematics. There is no "official line" and anyone with ideas and the energy to write them up is welcome to the fray.

How Have the Changes Been Received?

The various experimental texts have been used for several years in hundreds of schools throughout the country. Given properly trained teachers and able students, the results have been excellent. Freshmen entering universities are far better prepared than their counterparts of a few years ago. Teachers and students are enthusiastic, and there is much acclaim.

Some weaknesses, however, have appeared. The new materials are too hard for the less than average student, and so new versions are being written for these pupils. Some schools swung too far on the pendulum and forgot to teach skills as well as ideas. They have learned and are moving back toward a well-balanced position.

There has, however, been some outspoken opposition. Part of this comes from congenital conservatives who oppose change of any kind; part comes from those who are too lazy to change; part comes from the uniformed (who have not read this book!); and there is a small group of mathematicians who think that extremists have taken over the movement and are leading it into dangerous territory. Any revolution has its extreme fringe, and I agree that our extremists have gone too far. The opposition, however, is badly mistaken in its belief that these extremists represent the views of the great body of mathematics teachers. Judged by the published work of its responsible leaders, the revolution is on firm ground, and its success will bring tremendous benefits to the American people.

CHAPTER 3 WHAT YOUR SCHOOL CAN DO

Those of us who are involved in this movement are frequently called upon by somewhat bewildered school officials. Someone in the school system has got the word about the "new mathematics", perhaps a teacher who attended a summer institute, perhaps a curriculum supervisor who attended a national meeting, or perhaps a parent who is new to the district and knew what was happening in his former home town. These officials are naturally nervous, for they wish to do the right thing. But they are confused by the plethora of programs and initials, by the aggressive claims of salesmen of texts and equipment, and by their own inexperience with curriculum reform of this kind. So they come to us and ask for help. This chapter is a summary of the advice that I have given in many visits to school districts. I hope that it will be helpful to parents who wish to get action out of their local school people, or who wish to evaluate those actions which are being taken.

Become Familiar with the New Programs

The first step is to learn what all the shouting is about. Reading this book will help you, but you should also read the excellent pamphlets *The Revolution in School Mathematics* (1961) and *An Analysis of the New Mathematics Programs* (1963), which are published by the National Council of Teachers of Mathematics, 1201 Sixteenth Street N.W., Washington, D.C. 20036. Each pamphlet costs $0.50, and quantity discounts are available. These give the names, addresses, and points of view of the leading projects and people in the field. You can also obtain information from the mathematics department of your local university, and such departments are usually delighted to provide speakers at PTA's or the like to whom they can explain what is happening. Your state department of education can also be very helpful. A school district which does not have this basic information is very much behind the times.

It is not enough, however, for a few administrators, teachers, or parents to be familiar with the new alphabet soup; the mathematics teachers must also know something of the details. Even though they are completely new to the movement, teachers can get a good start on their own by reading the *Report of the Commission on Mathematics of the College Entrance Examination Board* together with its detailed appendix. Copies may be obtained from the Educational Testing Service, Princeton, New Jersey ($1.00). Teachers can also benefit greatly by working through one of the SMSG texts. The one titled *Mathematics for the Junior High School* is an excellent place to begin. These texts are available through the Yale University Press, 92A Yale Station, New Haven, Conn. (two parts, each $3.00). A profitable method of studying such a text is to organize an after-school faculty seminar in which teachers take turns presenting the new material to each other. When they have trouble, an occasional visit from someone in a local college will usually straighten them out.

Get the Support of Teachers, Administrators, School Board, and Parents

It is futile to try to begin one of the new programs without the approval and knowledge of all the interested people in the community. It is particularly dangerous for one school to change its curriculum without full consultation with others that may be affected. I have seen very serious difficulties, for example, when a junior high school started teaching algebra in the eighth grade without considering what would happen to these children when they entered a high school which disapproved of acceleration. Decisions of this kind must be system-wide and not piecemeal by schools.

The parents also need to be brought into the picture in advance. For there can be a bad reaction from home when Johnny shows off his algebra book, which is full of words and problems that father never learned about in school. Some school people take the view that telling parents anything is asking for trouble, but I strongly disagree. Parents are entitled to know what is going on in their schools, and if they are not informed they are quite unlikely to approve the special taxes needed to support the schools.

Make Certain the Teachers Are Retrained

Once a decision has been made to install a new program, the progress of events should not be too hasty. It is madness to hand even the best teacher one of the new books on September 1 and tell her to begin using it at once. The changes in approach, emphasis, and terminology are too great to be overcome quickly without outside help. Fortunately there are many avenues by which this help can be obtained. The school district should require that a teacher about to begin a new program attend a summer institute (such as those sponsored by the National Science Foundation) or a summer school in a university which offers appropriate courses in the new programs. School boards have even been known to pay the way of teachers so that they could take such courses.

Those teachers who cannot get to such summer schools can often find helpful courses or institutes offered by their local university in the late afternoons, evenings, or on Saturdays. These are also useful for those who have been to a summer institute, and who wish to enlarge on the training received there. Some school districts arrange for these extension courses to be held in regular school buildings, and frequently sponsor courses for inexperienced teachers which are taught by their more knowledgeable colleagues.

Do Not Start a Crash Program

The most dangerous man in the whole business is the eager beaver, hard-driving principal or superintendent who suddenly makes mathematics his special project for the year, and says, for example: "Put SMSG into every classroom in the schools, beginning at 9 o'clock tomorrow." Perhaps no such person exists, but I have met some that come mighty close. A good school curriculum in mathematics must be developed gradually; it should be watched constantly and improved and extended every year. A crash program which intends to do everything at once (and then get on with something "important" such as the new stadium) is sure to fail.

The Way to Start

Typical steps are these:

(1) Start with a few teachers and a few classes at strategic points in the curriculum such as the seventh and ninth grades. These teachers must have special training, and it is best if the classes are composed of the more able students.

(2) For the next year, train more teachers and expand the programs to the next grades (eighth and tenth, for example, from the seventh and ninth) and start a new group of students at the earlier levels. Continue expansion in this way.

(3) Gradually introduce the new materials into classes for the less able. At first only a few units may be inserted into a standard course, but these can be expanded as the teachers learn how to adapt them to the abilities of these children.

(4) As a final goal, have something new going on in every classroom in your system. This can easily require a development of five to ten years, but it must be done.

Distinguish Between New Mathematical Ideas
and Commercial Mechanical Aids

Some schools have missed the point of the mathematical revolution and have supposed that they can meet their obligations by buying various mechanical teaching aids. It is no wonder that this has happened, for NDEA (National Defense Education Act) money is plentiful, persuasive salesmen are everywhere, and it is so much easier to spend money than to change people. Beyond any doubt teaching can be improved through the use of appropriate audiovisual devices, but these devices are no substitute for a good curriculum. Let me discuss some of the more prominent of these devices.

1. BLOCKS.   There is nothing new about using blocks in the teaching of young children. These can be very effective in helping the youngsters to develop intuition about numbers and in enlarging their space perception. We have seen that the first step in learning is at the level of intuition, and that even simple abstractions such as the number "three" often come hard. It is here that blocks are most valuable.

Among the varieties of blocks available as aids in the teaching of arithmetic are some called Cuisenaire Rods. These are colored sticks 1 centimeter square and with lengths varying from 1 centimeter to 10 centimeters. By using these as concrete examples of nature, young children easily develop intuition about numbers, learn how to add, subtract, multiply, and divide with whole numbers, and later to handle the basic ideas of fractions. When these are used by a skillful teacher, the children make rapid progress in learning arithmetic with understanding. It is important, however, for the children to realize that the rods are merely a crutch to be used as they master arithmetic, and that the rods should be discarded as soon as they are no longer necessary.

Another valuable kind of blocks are those invented by Dr. Z. P. Dienes, called the Multibase Arithmetic Blocks. By means of these children learn the meaning of the positional notation in our number system (see Chapter 5) and rapidly acquire skills in computing in number systems to various bases.

Many teachers supplement or replace these commercial blocks with easily available counters such as milk bottle caps, pebbles, leaves, and the like. It is probably desirable to have a considerable variety of such materials on hand, for the main problem is to get the children to abstract from concrete objects to numbers themselves. This abstraction is easier if the children have had numerous different kinds of practical experiences.

It should be realized that all these aids contribute solely to the development of intuition. The additional steps of organization, deduction, and application are still necessary. Thus blocks, rods, pebbles, etc., no matter how useful, do not solve anything like all the problems of teaching arithmetic. Some schools seem to think that, by the single act of buying rods, they have done all that is needed to reform their arithmetic teaching. This is indeed an excellent first step, but it must be followed up by a change in the method of instruction as well.

2. TEACHING MACHINES. The past few years have seen the commercial exploitation of Professor B. F. Skinner's research on programed learning and teaching machines. The basic idea is very simple: students learn easily if they progress by very short steps, and if they are told immediately after each step whether their action was right or wrong. The questions which comprise these steps can be presented to the student as "frames" in a specially designed textbook, as films which he views in a teaching machine, or in many other ways.

The advantages claimed for this method are that students can proceed at their own pace independent of the rates of learning of their classmates, that learning is more rapid than in an ordinary class, that bad habits are stopped before they become ingrained, and that teachers are relieved from routine paper grading and hence are available to do more actual teaching. No one claims that the method is cheaper than the usual one, or that teachers will be any less important.

I am impressed with the probable usefulness of programed learning in many teaching situations, but I deplore the excesses of the commercial promoters of teaching machines. No matter how good the basic idea of programed learning may be, it cannot be proved in practice until some first-rate programs are written and tested experimentally. The construction of a program requires the collaboration of an experienced teacher and writer with a psychologist who is an expert in learning theory. Too often programs have been thrown together by less competent persons so that they could be available to promote the sale of teaching machines. The results have been unfortunate in many cases, and the reaction of mathematics teachers is quite mixed. Fortunately good programs following modern curricula in mathematics are now becoming available, and soon a better judgment can be made.

Moral: Do not rush into the purchase of teaching machines until you are sure that well-tested, modern programs are available for use in them. Consider programed textbooks quite carefully, but judge them by the same standards which you use in evaluating ordinary textbooks.

3. OVERHEAD PROJECTORS.   These are devices for projecting material which is in front of the teacher onto a screen above his head. These projectors can be very helpful in teaching visual subjects like geometry, for transparencies of geometric figures can be purchased (or prepared by the teacher) with much greater accuracy and appeal than drawings hastily drawn on the blackboard. Their use is especially recommended for the projection of drawings of solid figures when the students are being trained in space perception.

Moral: Do not buy overhead projectors unless you have enough money to buy transparencies and other supplies needed to make them effective.

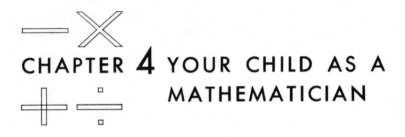

CHAPTER 4 YOUR CHILD AS A MATHEMATICIAN

Apart from a knowledge of the English language, competence in mathematics is the most useful skill which your child can acquire in school. Originally one of the three R's, its importance was played down in the heyday of progressive education on the ground that such a rigorous subject might interfere with the development of the child's personality. Events of the last ten years in the United States have restored mathematics to its old position as a subject which must be a major part of the education of every citizen, boy or girl.

The most striking feature of our times is that we are in the middle of the *Scientific Revolution*, which is rapidly transforming our whole society much as did the Industrial Revolution of the last century. No one can understand what is happening around him without a knowledge of science, and in order to learn about science one must first master mathematics. Indeed the situation is even more serious than that. Automation is sweeping our factories and offices, and jobs for the unskilled are rapidly disappearing. If your child does not master mathematics in the schools of today, he may well be among the unemployed of tomorrow. It is, therefore, the obligation of the schools to provide the best possible education in mathematics, and the duty of you as parents to see that your child is enrolled in mathematics throughout his entire school career.

Let us examine the mathematical preparation which is needed for a number of popular careers. It is perhaps commonplace that mathematics is required for a career as a physicist, chemist, or engineer, but few people outside the colleges realize that the mathematical requirements of these professions have doubled within the past decade. School counselors and parents will still do well to urge mathematics upon every prospective physical scientist or engineer, but they are not properly informed if they recommend less mathematics to prospective economists, psychologists, biologists, physicians, and business executives. Even the poet and the musician are not untouched by this cultural revolution.

World War II marks the turning point in the mathematical needs of workers in the behavioral sciences and in business. Between 1940 and 1943 the Nazi threat was so great that the military leaders of Great Britian and the United States turned to scientists (including mathematicians) to help plan the strategy of the war. This was the beginning of the discipline called *Operations Research* which in one form or another has become an essential feature of our business and industrial life. The basic method is that which I described in Chapter I: the scientists built a mathematical model of warfare and proceded to draw conclusions from this as to the proper conduct of the war. Since this was total war, we had to learn as much as possible about the economies of enemy countries. The purpose then was to destroy these economies, but we soon discovered how little economists knew about the interrelationship of the various portions of an industrial complex. We wanted to know what industries to bomb for maximum effect, but nobody could provide well-reasoned answers. After the war economists started to build mathematical models of a nation's economy in order to find such interrelationships for peaceful use and before they realized it they were head over heels into more mathematics than they had ever known to exist.

The war also spawned the mathematical subjects known as *Game Theory* and *Linear Programing*. These are serious efforts to help executives make decisions in a rational fashion rather than on the basis of customs, intuition, or the advice of "experts" from out of town. There has grown up a large and influential group who are practicing these arts under the general heading of *Management Science*.

A simultaneous development has been the perfection of the high-speed digital electronic computing machine. From their early beginnings during the war these machines have been refined and improved to an amazing extent. They are now essential equipment in scientific research organizations, industrial plants, and large businesses. Technical and management decisions are now made on the basis of data which are analyzed on these machines, and much guesswork has disappeared from our industrial and business operations. The business executive who cannot cope with this new type of precise decision making is likely to find himself bypassed for promotion or even out of a job.

I do not mean to say that every business man must know how to operate these machines, for with luck he can find technicians to do this. He must, however, understand what machines can do and what they cannot do. He must have a feeling for the quality of information which is fed into the machine, and be able to judge the reliability of its output. There is a popular worship of numbers which is far from justified; for there is much truth in the old saying: "Figures don't lie, but liars can figure." So that our executive will be able to avoid being misled by accidental or intentional errors of this kind, he needs to have facility with numbers and logic. He can obtain this by studying mathematics.

The future biologist or physician is faced with a revolution of major proportions in these subjects. The important discoveries in biology are now closely intertwined with modern chemistry and physics, and these require a deep knowledge of mathematics. The future physician will wish to build upon these discoveries in biology, and will also wish to understand the uses of high-speed computers in medical research and diagnosis. He cannot afford to be a mathematical cripple.

The literary man spends his life interpreting people and society through his essays, verse, stories, plays, and novels. When so much of our society is involved in the Scientific Revolution, the writer cannot make sound interpretations of society without understanding the fundamental ideas of science and mathematics. He need not acquire a large amount of skill, but he must have first-hand knowledge of the chief ideas and methods of thought.

Since the school boy or girl can hardly know how his later life will be spent, he should not avoid a subject which is as fundamental to so many careers as is mathematics.

What Mathematics Courses in High School?

Since all children in elementary schools are taught arithmetic, I need not argue for mathematics at this level. The real problem begins in the high school, where students have a choice in their academic programs. The basic principle is that mathematics should be studied *every year* throughout the entire educational process. We seem to have the idea that, once a course has been completed, the knowledge so acquired is permanent. Yet we all know how rapidly we forget anything that we do not practice continually, whether it is golf, piano playing, or book learning. Since your child will need his mathematics in his job or in college, he should maintain and expand his knowledge of it throughout the high school and on into college.

I know, of course, that large numbers of students drop mathematics after one or two years in high school; and it is to their parents that these remarks are directed. The usual reasons given for this practice are: (1) mathematics is hard, (2) they see no use for it, (3) the colleges do not require more mathematics for entrance, and (4) there are other subjects of greater interest or importance. I cannot deny that mathematics is hard, but so are most worth while intellectual activities. Students do not learn at the same rate, and those who are slower with mathematics are the earliest dropouts in our subject. The schools can help prevent this by offering mathematics at a variety of speeds and difficulty, so that every child can be placed in a class that suits his needs. I do not blame a youngster for being uninterested in a subject if he sees no relationship between it and his later life. If our children do not see this relationship in mathematics, our teaching needs reform, school counselors need to be indoctrinated, and parents must be educated.

The colleges have been negligent in setting their entrance standards to attract students rather than insisting on proper preparation for those who are admitted. These entrance requirements are

rapidly being raised, and in no case should they be interpreted as
the maximum preparation needed for college work. The competition
for time from other subjects does raise difficult problems. Mathematics is not the only subject a high school student should study,
and there is heavy pressure for more high school work in foreign
languages, natural science, and social science—not to mention fine
arts, driver education, and physical fitness. With careful planning,
however, there is still time to meet these pressures within a four-
year high school career. Normal students can carry four academic
subjects without difficulty, and the honors students can handle
five without strain. A typical program is the following:

English	4 years
Mathematics	4 years
Foreign language	3–4 years
Social science	3 years
Natural science	2 years
Nonacademic subjects	4 years
Total	20–21 years

This outline may be criticized in that only two years are
allocated to natural science. In my opinion it is wiser for a student
to take four years of mathematics than to expand his high school
work in science. For then he is prepared to understand fully the
more rigorous science courses which he will meet in college. In the
long run this program will put him farther ahead.

I should note, also, that the foreign language needs to be chosen
carefully. The future scientist must know French, German, *and*
Russian, and he should begin one of these in high school. Spanish
has many attractions, but it is a waste of time for the scientist.

I know that there will be static from parents and teachers
concerning the recommendations as they apply to the less mathematically gifted. Let it be understood that I do not propose to
drag these students unwillingly through the four-year mathematical
curriculum established for the mathematically able. Special programs adapted to their speeds and needs should be made available.
Indeed, it is these students for whom four years of work is most
important, for it takes them longer to acquire the skills needed for
survival in our age of automation. Moreover, it is not mandatory

that they study mathematics every day in the week. Tuesday-Thursday courses designed to maintain their skills can be dovetailed with Monday-Wednesday-Friday courses in other academic or nonacademic subjects. But again, their instruction in mathematics *must be continuous.*

Some of the difficulty with the mathematically less able arises from the misconception that a child is stupid if he cannot learn arithmetic. This leads to unpleasant scenes at home, and not infrequently to physical violence. Naturally such treatment prevents the child from learning mathematics; what he needs is help and encouragement rather than a sense of failure. The schools are learning how to deal with these individual differences, but the problem is far from solved.

Careers as a Mathematician

Let me turn now to the problems of the child who is really good at mathematics. Parents often ask me whether there is any future for them as professional mathematicians. The answer to this is a resounding "yes" for both boys and girls. Until recently the only way for a mathematician to make a living was for him to be a teacher at a school or college, but since the war the situation has changed completely. Industry, business, and government are now eager to find young mathematicians, and the colleges are bedeviled with recruiters from these companies. The supply is only a small fraction of the demand.

The most exciting jobs in industry are open only to Ph.D.'s, and so I urge young people to stay in graduate school as long as they are making the grade. Salaries at this level are very attractive, and working conditions are generally good. Mathematicians with bachelor's and master's degrees are also in heavy demand, especially in connection with high-speed computing machines. Girls compete equally with boys in such work. There are also opportunities for mathematics B.A.'s in insurance companies as actuaries. Employment as an actuary is an excellent introduction to the insurance business and often leads to promotion in the management of the company. Details of and current salaries in mathematical employment are contained in the pamphlet *Professional Opportunities in Mathematics,* available for $0.25 from the Mathematical

Association of America, University of Buffalo, Buffalo, New York, 14214.

I close with a word of caution about industrial mathematics. The mathematician in industry must work closely with other employees of the company and needs to be able to communicate with them. He must, therefore, have a substantial knowledge of what these other people are doing, and it would be wise for him to acquire this knowledge while he is in school. By this I mean, for example, that a prospective industrial mathematician should be well grounded in physics and portions of engineering, and that a prospective mathematician in business should know economics, accounting, etc. The pure mathematician without outside knowledge of these kinds is not likely to be useful or happy except in an academic environment.

CHAPTER 5 NUMBERS

With this chapter we begin an elementary survey of some of the important ideas in mathematics as it is now being taught in the schools. You will observe that most of this is familiar, and I doubt that you will have any trouble with it. The best place to begin the story is with numbers, for these are the foundation of our subject.

The most elementary numbers are those which are used in counting, namely: 1, 2, 3, 4, 5, ... These are called *counting numbers* or *natural numbers*. To these we should add 0 (zero), even though historically it was invented much later than the others. As we shall see, all other kinds of numbers are constructed by various devices out of these.

Properly speaking, the symbols 0, 1, 2, 3, 4, 5, . . . are names for numbers, rather than numbers themselves, and we prefer to call them *numerals*, a word which means a name for a number. Other civilizations have used different names for these numbers and hence had different systems of numerals. For example, the Romans used I for one, V for five, X for ten, XI for eleven, and so on. We owe our system of numerals to the Arabs.

Even in our system of numerals, we have many ways of representing the same number. For instance we can write "five" as $5, 1 + 4, 2 + 3, 7 - 2, {}^{10}\!/_2, \sqrt{25}$, etc.

Decimal Notation

A striking feature of our system of numerals is that it is based upon the number 10, apparently because most of us are born with ten fingers, which we use for counting. This notation is called the decimal system, and we shall see that we could have made many other choices. The decimal system is devised to use only the symbols $0, 1, 2, \ldots, 8, 9$, but their interpretations depend upon the *place* in which they are used. In order to give this interpretation we choose a *base* for our system, and in this case choose ten. We define $10^1 = 10$, $10^2 = 10 \times 10$, $10^3 = 10 \times 10 \times 10$, etc., and now are ready to define what is meant by a numeral such as 724. By definition:

$$724 = (7 \times 10^2) + (2 \times 10^1) + 4,$$
$$8216 = (8 \times 10^3) + (2 \times 10^2) + (1 \times 10^1) + 6,$$
$$57.3 = (5 \times 10) + (7) + \left(3 \times \frac{1}{10}\right),$$
$$2.458 = 2 + \left(4 \times \frac{1}{10^1}\right) + \left(5 \times \frac{1}{10^2}\right) + \left(8 \times \frac{1}{10^3}\right),$$

and so forth. As adults you are so familiar with this notation that you use it automatically without thinking. For the child, however, this use is not so automatic, and he must learn the fine points of the notation if he is to understand his arithmetic. Still, he knows enough of the notation so that it is hard for him to see the point of careful analysis. For this reason we use an unfamiliar base, say seven, to teach him the ideas of the place values of numerals.

In base seven, we use only the symbols $0, 1, \ldots, 6$ and define, for example:

$$413_{\text{seven}} = (4 \times 7^2) + (1 \times 7^1) + 3,$$

where 413_{seven} means the number represented by the numeral 413 to the base seven. Using this notation we can compute a table from which we can convert from base ten to base seven and vice versa:

Base Ten	Base Seven
1_{ten}	1_{seven}
2_{ten}	2_{seven}
3_{ten}	3_{seven}
4_{ten}	4_{seven}
5_{ten}	5_{seven}
6_{ten}	6_{seven}
7_{ten}	10_{seven}
8_{ten}	11_{seven}
9_{ten}	12_{seven}
10_{ten} etc.	13_{seven} etc.

In a similar fashion,

$$413_{seven} = (4 \times 7^2) + (1 \times 7) + 3 = 196 + 7 + 3$$
$$= 206_{ten}.$$

Also,

$$2164_{seven} = (2 \times 7^3) + (1 \times 7^2) + (6 \times 7) + 4$$
$$= 686 + 49 + 42 + 4$$
$$= 781_{ten}.$$

There is a convenient scheme for doing this sort of conversion in a compact form, known as *synthetic division*. Let me illustrate by redoing the illustrations above.

4	1	3	$\lfloor 7$		2	1	6	4	$\lfloor 7$
	28	203				14	105	777	
4	29	206			2	15	111	781	

The steps are these: Write down the base seven digits leaving spaces between them. Bring down the first of these to the bottom line unchanged. Multiply this by 7, and add the product to the second digit. Continue, moving to the right. The final sum is the appropriate numeral to base ten.

In order to proceed in the opposite direction, it is convenient to have a table of powers of seven available:

$$7^1 = 7,$$
$$7^2 = 49,$$
$$7^3 = 343,$$
$$7^4 = 2401.$$

Now let us find the expression to base seven of the numeral 1954_{ten}. We divide 1954 by the largest power of seven which goes into it, namely, $7^3 = 343$, and obtain

$$1954 = (5 \times 7^3) + 239.$$

We repeat the process by dividing 239 by $7^2 = 49$, and obtain

$$239 = (4 \times 7^2) + 43.$$

Finally

$$43 = (6 \times 7) + 1.$$

Assembling all these results we have

$$1954_{\text{ten}} = (5 \times 7^3) + (4 \times 7^2) + (6 \times 7) + 1$$
$$= 5461_{\text{seven}}.$$

In a similar fashion we find that

$$932_{\text{ten}} = (2 \times 7^3) + (5 \times 7^2) + (0 \times 7) + 1$$
$$= 2501_{\text{seven}}.$$

We can do arithmetic to the base seven just as easily as we can to base ten, provided that we remember what we are doing. Addition depends on the table:

ADDITION TABLE FOR BASE SEVEN
(All Numerals Are to Base Seven)

+	0	1	2	3	4	5	6
0	0	1	2	3	4	5	6
1	1	2	3	4	5	6	10
2	2	3	4	5	6	10	11
3	3	4	5	6	10	11	12
4	4	5	6	10	11	12	13
5	5	6	10	11	12	13	14
6	6	10	11	12	13	14	15

Now let us add the following where all numerals are to the base seven:

45
+26

Adding in the usual way we find that $5 + 6 = 14$, which means one seven plus four. We write the four and carry the one into the second column:

$$
\begin{array}{r}
1 \\
45 \\
+26 \\
\hline
4
\end{array}
$$

We add the second column and get $4 + 2 = 6$ and $6 + 1 = 10$. So we have, finally,

$$
\begin{array}{r}
45 \\
+26 \\
\hline
104
\end{array}
$$

It is a good exercise to convert all these numerals to base ten and check this answer. [Result: $33 + 20 = 53_{\text{ten}}$.]

Similarly, we can do multiplication to base seven. The multiplication table is as shown.

MULTIPLICATION TABLE FOR BASE SEVEN
(All Numerals Are to Base Seven)

×	0	1	2	3	4	5	6
0	0	0	0	0	0	0	0
1	0	1	2	3	4	5	6
2	0	2	4	6	11	13	15
3	0	3	6	12	15	21	24
4	0	4	11	15	22	26	33
5	0	5	13	21	26	34	42
6	0	6	15	24	33	42	51

We can multiply in the usual fashion using this table; for example, let us compute

$$34_{\text{seven}} \times 25_{\text{seven}}.$$

The process reads as follows:

$$
\begin{array}{r}
34 \\
25 \\
\hline
236 \\
101 \\
\hline
1246
\end{array}
$$

Here we multiplied 5 times 4 and got 26. We wrote the 6 and
carried the 2. Then 5 times 3 = 21, to which we added the carried
2 to obtain 23. In the next line 2 times 4 = 11; we write 1 and
carry 1. Then 2 times 3 = 6, to which we add the carried 1 to
write 10. Now add the two rows using the addition table. [Check:
In base ten, this problem becomes $25 \times 19 = 475$.]

High-speed computers commonly do their internal arithmetic
in base two notation. Here we use only the numerals 0 and 1, and
these are represented electronically by voltages, one "high", one
"low". A short conversion table is as shown.

Base Ten	Base Two
1_{ten}	1_{two}
2_{ten}	10_{two}
3_{ten}	11_{two}
4_{ten}	100_{two}
5_{ten}	101_{two}
6_{ten}	110_{two}
7_{ten}	111_{two}
8_{ten}	1000_{two}

Arithmetic in base two is very simple but tedious. The addition
and multiplication tables are as follows:

+	0	1		×	0	1
0	0	1		0	0	0
1	1	10		1	0	1

These are easy to remember, but even simple computations are
lengthy when done by hand. For example consider $6_{ten} \times 5_{ten}$ in
base two notation. We must compute

$$
\begin{array}{r}
110 \\
\times 101 \\
\hline
110 \\
000 \\
110 \\
\hline
11110
\end{array}
$$

where the numerals are in base two. We then verify that

$$11,110_{two} = (1 \times 2^4) + (1 \times 2^3) + (1 \times 2^2) + (1 \times 2) + 0$$
$$= 16 + 8 + 4 + 2$$
$$= 30_{ten}.$$

Arithmetic to base two is frequently called *binary* arithmetic.

By contrast, we could choose a large base, say sixty, for our arithmetic. Then we would need sixty different numerical symbols, and learning the addition and multiplication tables would be an enormous job. But once they were learned, arithmetic computations would be very simple. Our decimal system seems to be a good compromise between these extremes.

Negative Numbers

If no one ever ran a deficit, or if the temperature were always comfortably warm, these counting numbers would serve for the normal purposes of business. But deficits do appear, and red ink is not always available, so we must extend our number system. The convenient device is the introduction of the negative integers: -1, -2, -3, -4, . . . , which are defined to satisfy the equations

$$1 + (-1) = 0,$$
$$2 + (-2) = 0,$$
$$3 + (-3) = 0,$$
$$\text{etc.}$$

When you went to school, it was customary to read -2 as *minus two*, but now some authors call it *negative two*. The reason is that "minus" connotes the idea of subtraction, whereas we are not subtracting here at all. As I shall explain in Chapter 7, the minus sign has several distinct meanings in mathematics, and so it is helpful to distinguish among these, at least in the early stages of algebra. After these negative numbers have been introduced, it is necessary to settle on rules for their arithmetic. As we shall see in Chapter 8, these rules are by no means arbitrary, but are derived from other properties of numbers which I shall discuss in that chapter.

Rational Numbers

We are also used to the appearance of common fractions in our daily lives, and it is necessary to expand our number system to include these. There are many approaches to fractions, but the most direct is to define $\frac{3}{4}$, say, as a number such that

$$(\tfrac{3}{4}) \times 4 = 3.$$

More generally, we must define a/b where a and b are integers (positive or negative, with b different from zero). This is defined to be a number such that

$$(a/b) \times b = a.$$

Numbers of this kind are called *rational*, since they are expressed by means of a ratio.

You will observe that there are many names, or numerals, for the same rational number. For example:

$$\frac{1}{2}, \quad \frac{2}{4}, \quad \frac{3}{6}, \quad \frac{500}{1000}, \quad \text{etc.},$$

can all be used to represent the rational number which we call *one-half*. When we write the decimal expansion of a rational number, we find that after a certain number of places the digits begin reappearing in cycles. For example,

$$\begin{aligned}
\tfrac{1}{3} &= 0.333 \ldots , \\
\tfrac{1}{4} &= 0.25000 \ldots , \\
\tfrac{1}{7} &= 0.142857142857 \ldots .
\end{aligned}$$

Decimals of this kind are called *repeating decimals*. Conversely, any decimal whose digits repeat in cycles can be expressed in the form a/b, and therefore is a numeral representing a rational number.

Real Numbers

In ancient times the Pythagoreans believed that all numbers were necessarily rational, and that a harmonious human relationship could always be expressed by numbers of the form a/b where a and b were small integers. This belief was exploded when it was shown that there is no rational number whose square is 2, that is, that $\sqrt{2}$ must be irrational. In order to make room for such numbers, we again expand the number system by including *nonrepeating* as well repeating decimal expansions. The collection of all such numbers is called the *real number system*.

The adjective *real* is quite misleading here, but is so well imbedded in usage that it cannot be replaced. The real numbers are high-order abstractions from nature, and are far from "real" in the customary sense of this word. The word "real" is used to distinguish these from another system of numbers which our ancestors called *imaginary*. Imaginary numbers arose because of the problem of introducing $\sqrt{-1}$ into algebra. Since there is no real number whose square is negative, $\sqrt{-1}$ was completely excluded from consideration for many centuries. Then it began to creep in as an *imaginary* number. We are now so used to it that we treat it like any other abstract number, but the traditional names have stayed with us.

In order to complete our number system, finally we introduce *complex numbers* of the form $a + bi$, where a and b are real and i is a symbol that stands for $\sqrt{-1}$. As before, the word "complex" is a misnomer derived from our ancestors; it is an inappropriate name, but we are now stuck with it. We add and subtract these numbers as in the illustrations:

$$(2 + 3i) + (4 + 7i) = 6 + 10i,$$
$$(1 - i) - (2 + 5i) = -1 - 6i.$$

In multiplying two complex numbers, we proceed by ordinary algebra, and then replace i^2 by -1 in the next to last step. For instance,

$$
\begin{aligned}
(3 + 5i) \times (4 + 2i) &= (3 \times 4) + (3 \times 2i) + (5i \times 4) + (5i \times 2i) \\
&= 12 + 6i + 20i + 10i^2 \\
&= 12 + 26i + 10i^2 \\
&= 12 + 26i + 10(-1) \\
&= 2 + 26i.
\end{aligned}
$$

Since most of you have no occasion to use complex numbers in your daily lives, you may wonder why we bother with them or why your children should be asked to learn them. Although there are practical uses for complex numbers in science and engineering, the most important reason for discussing them is purely aesthetic. In elementary algebra we find that we can solve any equation of the form

$$ax + b = 0,$$

where a and b are real numbers and $a \neq 0$. Indeed, the solution is

$$x = -\frac{b}{a}.$$

We run into difficulty, however, if we try to solve

$$ax^2 + bx + c = 0,$$

where a, b, and c are real numbers and $a \neq 0$.
For in particular

$$x^2 + 1 = 0$$

is a special case of such an equation, and it is not satisfied by any real number x. It is awkward and inelegant to have to admit that simple equations of this kind do not have solutions. So we introduce complex numbers to provide these solutions. We can then prove that there is always at least one complex number x which satisfies our quadratic equation

$$ax^2 + bx + c = 0.$$

You might think that we would have to introduce fancier and fancier kinds of numbers to solve equations of higher degree such as

$$x^3 + 2x^2 + x + 1 = 0,$$

or

$$3x^4 + 4x^3 - x^2 - x + 6 = 0.$$

It is remarkable, indeed, that complex numbers still do the job, so that we need not introduce further systems of numbers for such purposes.

The use of the terms *real*, *imaginary*, and *complex* is an illustration of how mathematical terminology differs from ordinary English. These and only these words are proper mathematical language for the ideas involved, and common English synonyms cannot be substituted for them. One of the more amusing but frustrating confusions of this type occurred several years ago in connection with a mathematical manuscript. This was being edited by a professional editor for publication as a book. The editor found the use of "real" repetitive and awkward, and so "genuine" was substituted for "real" in numerous places. Similarly, "complicated" was thought to be better English than "complex", and the substitution was made. As a result the manuscript became unintelligible to both layman and mathematician alike. So you must learn the special vocabulary of mathematics if you wish to read mathematics. There is no use fighting against it or trying to use substitutes. There are no short cuts, but it is not all that hard anyway.

PROBLEMS

1. Write the following in base ten notation. (a) 456_{seven}; (b) 5623_{seven}; (c) 206_{seven}.

2. Write the following in base seven notation. (a) 2196_{ten}; (b) 4503_{ten}; (c) 7203_{ten}.

3. Carry out the indicated operations on the understanding that all numerals are expressed to *base seven*. Then convert the given numerals to *base ten*, repeat the arithmetic, and check your answer.

(a)	25	(b)	513	(c)	36	(d)	432
	16		642		$\times 15$		$\times 23$
	+32		+135				

4. Write the following in base ten notation. (a) $10,110_{two}$; (b) $1,110,001_{two}$; (c) $1,100,101_{two}$.

5. Write the following in base two notation. (a) 46_{ten}; (b) 123_{ten}; (c) 256_{ten}.

6. Carry out the indicated operations on the understanding that all numerals are expressed to *base two*. Then convert the given numerals to *base ten*, repeat the arithmetic, and check your answer.

(a)	11	(b)	111	(c)	111	(d)	1011
	10		101		$\times 11$		$\times 101$
	+1		100				
			+11				

7. Write the addition and multiplication tables for numerals expressed in base three notation.

8. Use the tables obtained in Prob. 7 to carry out the following operations where the numerals are in *base three* notation. Check as directed in Probs. 3 and 6.

(a)	12	(b)	121	(c)	121	(d)	1222
	21		210		$\times 21$		$\times 112$
	+11		+112				

9. Express as repeating decimals (numerals are to base ten):
   (a) $\frac{1}{2}$; (b) $\frac{2}{3}$; (c) $\frac{2}{9}$; (d) $\frac{5}{11}$; (e) $1\frac{3}{7}$.

10. Carry out the following operations on complex numbers (numerals are to base ten):
    (a) $(1 + 4i) + (2 + 6i)$ (d) $(-4 + 5i) - (7 + 6i)$
    (b) $(2 - 2i) + (-5 + 3i)$ (e) $(3 + i) \times (2 - 3i)$
    (c) $(4 - i) - (2 + 3i)$ (f) $(1 + i) \times (1 - i)$

11. Show that $2 + 3i$ and $2 - 3i$ satisfy the equation

$$x^2 - 4x + 13 = 0$$

where all numerals are to base ten.

Problems 12–15 are not covered in the text, but if you think hard you should be able to solve them.

12. Write the following in *base ten* notation: (a) 35.2_{seven}; (b) 21.13_{seven}; (c) 101.1_{two}; (d) 110.11_{two}.

13. Carry out the following operations on the understanding that all numerals are expressed to *base seven*. Check as directed in Probs. 3 and 6.
    (a) $6\overline{)66}$ (d) $45\overline{)1353}$

    (b) $21\overline{)630}$ (e) 3426
                                                          -1645

    (c) $16\overline{)643}$ (f) 1536
                                                            -642

14. Express in the form a/b (all numerals are to base ten):
    (a) $0.44444\ldots$ *Hint:* Let $x = 0.4444\ldots$;
                          then $10x = 4.4444\ldots$,
                          so $9x = 4.0000\ldots$,
                          $x = \frac{4}{9}$;
    (b) $0.7777\ldots$; (c) $0.121212\ldots$; (d) $1.232323\ldots$.

15. (a) $\dfrac{3 + 4i}{2 + i}$ *Hint:* Try $\dfrac{3 + 4i}{2 + i} \times \dfrac{2 - i}{2 - i}$;   (b) $\dfrac{1 + 2i}{3 - 4i}$.

16. Show that $\dfrac{a + ib}{c + id} = \dfrac{(ac + bd) + i(bc - ad)}{c^2 + d^2}$.

ANSWERS

1. (a) 237_{ten}; (b) 2026_{ten}; (c) 104_{ten}.
2. (a) 6255_{seven}; (b) $16,062_{\text{seven}}$; (c) $30,000_{\text{seven}}$.

3. (a) 106_{seven}; (b) 1623_{seven}; (c)

$$
\begin{array}{r}
36 \\
\times 15 \\
\hline
252 \\
36 \\
\hline
642_{seven}
\end{array}
$$

(d)

$$
\begin{array}{r}
432 \\
\times 23 \\
\hline
1626 \\
1164 \\
\hline
13566_{seven}
\end{array}
$$

Check:

(a)
$$
\begin{array}{r}
19 \\
13 \\
23 \\
\hline
55_{ten}
\end{array}
$$

(b)
$$
\begin{array}{r}
255 \\
324 \\
75 \\
\hline
654_{ten}
\end{array}
$$

(c)
$$
\begin{array}{r}
27 \\
\times 12 \\
\hline
54 \\
27 \\
\hline
324_{ten}
\end{array}
$$

(d)
$$
\begin{array}{r}
219 \\
\times 17 \\
\hline
1533 \\
219 \\
\hline
3723_{ten}
\end{array}
$$

4. (a) 22_{ten}; (b) 113_{ten}; (c) 101_{ten}.

5. (a) $101,110_{two}$; (b) $1,111,011_{two}$; (c) $100,000,000_{two}$.

6. (a) 110_{two}; (b) $10,011_{two}$; (c)

$$
\begin{array}{r}
111 \\
\times 11 \\
\hline
111 \\
111 \\
\hline
10101_{two}
\end{array}
$$

(d)

$$
\begin{array}{r}
1011 \\
\times 101 \\
\hline
1011 \\
1011 \\
\hline
110111_{two}
\end{array}
$$

Check:

(a)
$$
\begin{array}{r}
3 \\
2 \\
1 \\
\hline
6_{ten}
\end{array}
$$

(b)
$$
\begin{array}{r}
7 \\
5 \\
4 \\
3 \\
\hline
19_{ten}
\end{array}
$$

(c) $7 \times 3 = 21_{ten}$; (d) $11 \times 5 = 55_{ten}$.

7.

+	0	1	2
0	0	1	2
1	1	2	10
2	2	10	11

×	0	1	2
0	0	0	0
1	0	1	2
2	0	2	11

8. (a) 121_{three}; (b) 1220_{three}; (c)

$$
\begin{array}{r}
121 \\
\times 21 \\
\hline
121 \\
1012 \\
\hline
11011_{three}
\end{array}
$$

(d)

$$
\begin{array}{r}
1222 \\
\times 112 \\
\hline
10221 \\
1222 \\
1222 \\
\hline
1000111_{three}
\end{array}
$$

Check:

(a)
$$
\begin{array}{r}
5 \\
7 \\
4 \\
\hline
16_{ten}
\end{array}
$$

(b)
$$
\begin{array}{r}
16 \\
21 \\
14 \\
\hline
51_{ten}
\end{array}
$$

(c) $16 \times 7 = 112_{ten}$; (d) $53 \times 14 = 742_{ten}$.

9. (a) $0.5000 \ldots$; (b) $0.6666 \ldots$; (c) $0.2222 \ldots$;
(d) $0.454545 \ldots$; (e) $1.428571428571 \ldots$.

10. (a) $3 + 10i$; (b) $-3 + i$; (c) $2 - 4i$; (d) $-11 - i$; (e) $9 - 7i$; (f) 2.

11. $(2 + 3i)^2 - 4(2 + 3i) + 13 = (-5 + 12i) - (8 + 12i) + 13 = 0$.

12. (a) $(26\frac{2}{7})_{ten}$; (b) $(15\frac{10}{49})_{ten}$; (c) $(5\frac{1}{2})_{ten}$; (d) $(6\frac{3}{4})_{ten}$.

13.

$$\overset{11_{seven}}{\text{(a) } 6\overline{)66}}
\qquad
\overset{30_{seven}}{\text{(b) } 21\overline{)630}}
\qquad
\overset{34_{seven}}{\text{(c) } 16\overline{)643}}$$

$$\begin{array}{r}
54 \\ \hline
103 \\
103 \\ \hline
\end{array}$$

$$\overset{22_{seven}}{\text{(d) } 45\overline{)1353}}
\qquad
\text{(e) } 1451_{seven};
\qquad
\text{(f) } 564_{seven}.$$

$$\begin{array}{r}
123 \\ \hline
123 \\
123 \\ \hline
\end{array}$$

Check:

$$\overset{8_{ten}}{\text{(a) } 6\overline{)48}}
\qquad
\overset{21_{ten}}{\text{(b) } 15\overline{)315}}
\qquad
\overset{25_{ten}}{\text{(c) } 13\overline{)325}}$$

$$\overset{16_{ten}}{\text{(d) } 33\overline{)528}}
\qquad
\text{(e) } \begin{array}{r} 1245 \\ -670 \\ \hline 575_{ten} \end{array}
\qquad
\text{(f) } \begin{array}{r} 615 \\ -324 \\ \hline 291_{ten} \end{array}$$

14. (a) $\frac{4}{9}$; (b) $\frac{7}{9}$; (c) $\frac{4}{33}$; (d) $1\frac{23}{99}$.

15. (a) $2 + i$; (b) $\dfrac{-1 + 2i}{5}$.

CHAPTER 6 SETS, FUNCTIONS, AND RELATIONS

Before introducing the main ideas to be discussed in this chapter, let us look at the problem of building a course of study in arithmetic and algebra which will extend in a systematic fashion from the early grades through the high school. My first observation is that arithmetic and school algebra are only names for two parts of the same subject, that artificial distinctions between them only serve to confuse everyone, and that we must consider these as a single subject when we plan a twelve-year curriculum.

The first steps in instruction in the early grades will be concerned with the properties of numbers. I have already mentioned the need for an intuitive approach at the outset in which concrete materials such as blocks, pebbles, leaves, etc., are used to help develop a proper feeling for the subject. Gradually intuition leads to a more systematic treatment of numbers, including the basic skills in arithmetic and the fine points of positional notation which I discussed in the last chapter. For a further advance into what is commonly called algebra, an organization and simplification of the ideas and facts of arithmetic are now essential. Before we are finished we need to construct a full mathematical model of arithmetic and algebra of the type which I described in Chapter 1. Remember the two essentials: (1) careful terminology (both undefined and defined), and (2) statements of general relationships which are commonly called axioms. The traditional textbooks in algebra have been weak on both of these counts, and much that may seem new to you as parents has been introduced to remedy these faults.

In introducing terminology it is necessary to walk a fine line between confusion and pedantry. Some mathematicians have been so revolted at the sloppy use of words in the older books that they have adopted language so artificial and complicated that almost no one can understand them. Some teachers have interpreted the "new mathematics" as being little more than a fancy vocabulary which must be learned if one wishes to join the club, and they have thus missed all the main points of the current reform movement. What is needed is a sensible intermediate position whose objectives are clarity, understanding, and simplicity. In this chapter I shall discuss how this is accomplished in one important area of our subject. In the next chapter I shall turn to the general principles of algebra which can be introduced once the language is clear.

Sets

The use of the word "set" is perhaps the most controversial topic in the current reform movement. Some think that this one word separates the conservatives from the radicals: if you do not use sets, you are an old fogy; if you do, you are up to date. This oversimplification of the facts ignores the essential matter of how sets are used. Before I can explain this problem to you, I must explain what a set is.

The idea of a set permeates all mathematics, for it is a short word which means a group, a collection, or an aggregate of numbers, lines, points, etc. It is thus clear and elementary. Those objects which belong to a set are called its *elements* or *members;* for instance, Lincoln is a member or element of the set of presidents of the United States.

Let us begin with some examples of sets and the notation for them.

(1) $\{1, 6, 15\}$ is the set whose elements are the numbers 1, 6, and 15. We use braces $\{\ \ \}$ to represent sets in this way.

(2) $\{1, 2, 3, 4, \ldots\}$ is the set of all natural numbers.

(3) $\{$Bob, Jim, Bill$\}$ is a set of boys whose last name is Allendoerfer.

(4) $\{x | x^2 = 1\}$. This notation is to be read "The set of numbers x such that $x^2 = 1$." The vertical bar stands for "such that". This set can also be written $\{-1, 1\}$.

(5) $\varnothing$, the empty set which contains no elements. An example of such a set is the set of men born in 1700 who are still alive.

(6) $\{x | x^2 - 5x + 6 = 0\}$, the set of solutions of the equation $x^2 - 5x + 6 = 0$, namely, $\{2, 3\}$.

(7) $[a, b]$, a special notation for the set of all real numbers which lie between a and b inclusive, that is, those which satisfy the inequalities $a \leq x \leq b$. This set is called a *closed interval*.

(8) $]a, b[$, a special notation for the set of real numbers satisfying $a < x < b$. This set is called an *open interval*.

(9) $\{(x, y) | 3x - 4y + 12 = 0\}$. This notation requires some further explanation. The symbol (x, y) stands for a pair of numbers, x and y; moreover, it is understood that the pair (x, y) is to be distinguished from the pair (y, x)—that is, the order of the two numbers in the pair is of importance to us. For this reason we call (x, y) an *ordered pair* of numbers. The set defined above is, therefore, the set of those ordered pairs (x, y) whose components x and y satisfy the equation $3x - 4y + 12 = 0$. Examples of elements of this set are $(-4, 0)$, $(0, 3)$, $(8, 9)$; there are in fact infinitely many such pairs, and so we can never write down a complete list of them.

(10) $\{(x, y, z) | 3x - 4y + 6z + 12 = 0\}$. By analogy with (9) we call (x, y, z) an ordered triple. The elements of this set are those ordered triples whose components satisfy the given equation.

Examples (9) and (10) raise a special problem in that it is not possible to give a complete list of the elements of the given sets or to use a notation such as in (2) to suggest what these elements are. Thus we must invent another technique to help us see what the set is; namely, we construct the *graph of the set*. To do this we draw two perpendicular lines in the plane, as in Fig. 5, which we label the X-axis and the Y-axis. We plot the point P as the graph of the ordered pair (x, y) by measuring x units along the X-axis and y units along the Y-axis. Along the X-axis we measure to the right of O if x is positive and to the left if x is negative. Similarly, along the Y-axis, positive y are measured above O and negative y below O. Thus we have a point in the plane corresponding uniquely to each ordered pair of numbers (x, y). The graph of $\{(x, y) | 3x - 4y + 12 = 0\}$ is then the set of points in the plane, each of which is the graph of an

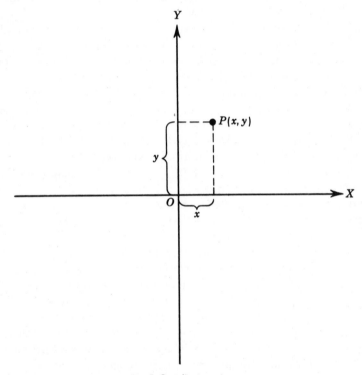

Fig. 5. Coordinate system.

ordered pair of numbers (x, y) whose components satisfy $3x - 4y + 12 = 0$. It can be proved that for an equation of this type (in which x and y occur to the first power only) the graph is a straight line as in Fig. 6.

We can do the same thing for the set in (10), but here we require three dimensions. We set up axes as in Fig. 7 and find a unique point corresponding to each ordered triple (x, y, z). We can prove that the graph of a set such as $\{(x, y, z)|3x - 4y + 6z + 12 = 0\}$ is a plane in our space.

In both of these cases the graph helps us to visualize the given set, but it is *not* the given set. There are two sets involved in our discussion of (9). First, we have the set of ordered pairs of numbers

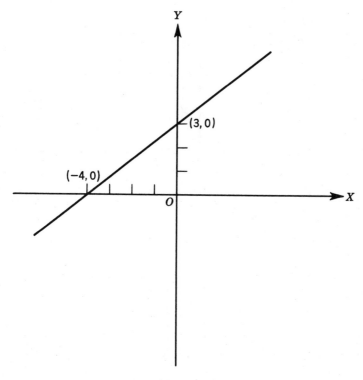

Fig. 6. Graph of $\{(x, y)|3x - 4y + 12 = 0\}$.

(x, y) which satisfy the given equation. Second, we have the set of points in the plane which lie along the graph we have plotted. These two sets are closely related in that to each pair (x, y) there corresponds a unique point, and to each point there corresponds a unique pair (x, y). Situations like this occur in many other places in mathematics, and so it is worth while for us to give a name to such a correspondence.

ONE TO ONE CORRESPONDENCE. Two sets $A = \{a_1, a_2, a_3, \ldots\}$ and $B = \{b_1, b_2, b_3, \ldots\}$ are said to be in 1 to 1 correspondence if and only if there exists a pairing of the a's and b's such that each a

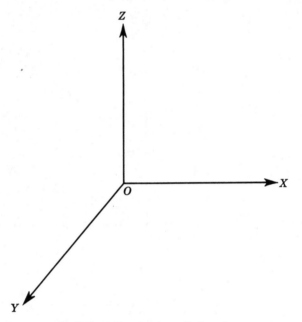

Fig. 7. Three-dimensional coordinate system.

corresponds to one and only one b and each b corresponds to one and only one a. We write such correspondences in several ways. For example,

John	Jim	Jerry
↕	↕	↕
Bill	Bob	Bert

represents a 1 to 1 correspondence between the sets John, Jim, Jerry and Bill, Bob, Bert. Another such correspondence is

John	Jim	Jerry
↕	↕	↕
Bob	Bert	Bill

If we assign the integer $2n$ to each positive integer n, we thus establish the 1 to 1 correspondence $n \leftrightarrow 2n$ or

$$
\begin{array}{ccccc}
1 & 2 & 3 & 4 & 5 \quad \cdots \\
\updownarrow & \updownarrow & \updownarrow & \updownarrow & \updownarrow \\
2 & 4 & 6 & 8 & 10 \quad \cdots
\end{array}
$$

between the set of positive integers and the set of even positive integers.

This notion of a 1 to 1 correspondence is well understood by children, even though they do not know the name for it. Indeed, the process of counting on one's fingers is based precisely on this idea, for this establishes a 1 to 1 correspondence between fingers and the objects to be counted.

Let me use examples (9) and (10) to illustrate how set notation can clear up ambiguities which frequently bother students. In the traditional books students are asked to "Graph the line $3x - 4y + 12 = 0$" or to "Graph the plane $3x - 4y + 6z + 12 = 0$". This causes no great problem, but difficulties arise when we consider the equation of a plane in which the coefficient of z is zero, such as $3x - 4y + 12 = 0$. Such planes are parallel to the Z-axis. You can already see the confusion: Is the graph of $3x - 4y + 12 = 0$ a *line* or a *plane* parallel to the Z-axis? The answer depends on the point of view or the instructions given with the problem. Unfortunately on tests or sets of review problems there can easily be ambiguity regarding the meaning of "Plot the graph of $3x - 4y + 12 = 0$." This can easily be clarified by using set language:

Plot the graph of $\{(x, y)|3x - 4y + 12 = 0\}$ (two dimensional)

or

Plot the graph of $\{(x, y, z)|3x - 4y + 12 = 0\}$ (three dimensional)

Students greatly appreciate having problems stated in unambiguous language so that they can search for the solution without having to try to guess what it was that the teacher or textbook had in mind. Set notation is one tool that helps to make such clarity possible.

Perhaps another example of the use of set language would be appropriate. In geometry students are faced with *locus problems*. A simple illustration is: "Find the locus of a point in the plane which moves so that its distance from a fixed point is a constant." The answer, of course, is "a circle". There are two troubles, however, with this statement of the problem. First, the word *locus* is unfamiliar and is usually not well understood. In any case it is a special word that needs careful explanation. Second, there is the reference to motion of a point. In physics particles do move, but in mathematics a point is not a particle and its motion is at best a pseudophysical idea and not a mathematical idea. The situation becomes clearer and more precise if we formulate it in set language: "Given a fixed point O in the plane, find the set of points P in the plane such that the distances PO are all equal." If the concept of *set* is understood, there are no unfamiliar words and no fuzzy problem with motion. This is the way mathematics should be written.

Doing Things with Sets

Mathematics is much more, however, than a collection of words and definitions. After we know what the words mean, we must do something with them. We must then turn to doing things with sets.

First we need to be clear on the matter of when two sets, described in possibly different ways, are the same, or are *identical*.

1. IDENTITY.   Two sets are said to be identical if and only if they contain precisely the same elements. The order in which these elements are written is immaterial. In such a situation we write $A = B$. For example,

$$\{6, 1, 9, 2\} = \{1, 2, 6, 9\},$$
$$\{x | x^2 = 1\} = \{-1, 1\}.$$

In the succeeding paragraphs I shall define other operations or ideas which are useful in working with sets.

2. SUBSET.   A set A is a subset of a set B if and only if every element of A is an element of B. The notation for this is $A \subseteq B$, read "A is a subset of B." When B contains elements that are not in A, we write $A \subset B$ and say that A is a proper subset of B.

For example,

$$\{1, 6, 12\} \subset \{1, 2, 6, 12, 15\},$$
$$\{2, 4, 6, 8, \ldots\} \subset \{1, 2, 3, 4, 5, \ldots\}.$$

The set of all red-haired girls is a proper subset of the set of all girls.

3. UNIVERSAL SET. Within a fixed mathematical framework such as algebra or geometry, we are dealing with sets whose elements are members of some large, fixed set, called the *universal set, U*. For example, U may be the set of all real numbers, the set of all points in the plane, etc. The specific sets with which we deal will then be subsets of U.

4. COMPLEMENT. Let A be a subset of the universal set U. Then its complement, written A', is the set of all elements of U which are not members of A. As an illustration, let U be the set of all integers, and A be the set of even integers. Then A' is the set.of odd integers. Or, let U be the set of all living people and A be the set of all blind people. Then A' is the set of all people who can see.

5. UNION OF TWO SETS. The union of sets A and B, written $A \cup B$, is the set of those elements which are members of A or B or both

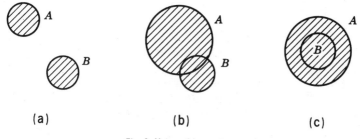

(a)   (b)   (c)

Fig. 8. Union of two sets.

A and B. The idea is illustrated in Fig. 8 for pairs of subsets of the plane. The union of A and B is shaded.

For example, let A be the set of positive integers and B be the set of integers whose square is 4. Then $A \cup B$ is the set $\{-2, 1, 2, 3, 4 \ldots\}$.

As another example, let A be the set of red-haired girls and B be the set of blue-eyed girls. Then $A \cup B$ is the set of girls who have red hair, blue eyes, or both.

6. INTERSECTION OF TWO SETS. The intersection of sets A and B, written $A \cap B$, is the set of those elements which are members of both A and B. See Fig. 9 for an illustration of this idea. $A \cap B$ is shaded. For example, let A be the set of red-headed girls, and B be

the set of blue-eyed girls. Then $A \cap B$ is the set of red-headed girls who also have blue eyes. As another example, if $A = \{1, 6, 9, 12\}$, $B = \{9, 12, 15\}$, then

$$A \cap B = \{9, 12\}.$$

Now let us apply these ideas to some familiar problems in mathematics. You are used to questions such as "What is the solution of $x^2 + 7x + 12 = 0$?" but before attempting an answer we must understand the problem. In the first place we call x a *variable*, and we need to say what "variable" means.

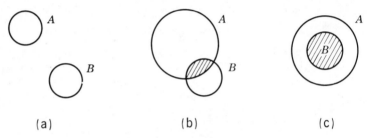

(a)   (b)   (c)

Fig. 9. Intersection of two sets.

7. VARIABLE.   A variable is a symbol which may be replaced in a mathematical expression by any element of a given universal set. Some authors say that a variable is a *place holder* which may then be replaced by any element of U.

A formula (or a sentence) containing a variable is called an *open sentence* if after the variable is replaced by an element of U there results a formula which can be meaningfully called true or false. For example,

$$x + 3 = 5$$

is an open sentence. For when $x = 4$ we have

$$4 + 3 = 5 \qquad \text{(which is false),}$$

but when $x = 2$ we have

$$2 + 3 = 5 \qquad \text{(which is true).}$$

8. TRUTH SET.   The truth set of an open sentence is the set of elements in U whose substitution for the variable in the open sentence

gives true statements. For example, the truth set of

$$x^2 + 7x + 12 = 0$$

is the set $\{-3, -4\}$. The truth set of

  x was president of the United States on Jan. 1, 1964

is the set {Lyndon B. Johnson}. In general we write truth sets in the notation:

$$\{x|x^2 + 7x + 12 = 0\},$$
$$\{x|x^2 > 4\},$$
$$\{(x,\ y)|2x + 4y - 6 = 0\}.$$

Thus the notion of a truth set includes the familiar idea of the solution of an equation, but it is a broader concept. It applies to inequalities and to open sentences in two or more variables, such as

$$\{x|x^2 + 5x + 6 > 0\},$$
$$\{(x,\ y)|3x + 4y - 5 = 0\},$$
$$\{(x,\ y)|x^2 + y^2 < 1\}.$$

Thus by using this notation we can formulate an important class of mathematical problems in a precise fashion, namely, we are asked to find the truth sets of given open sentences.

As an illustration of the use of the concept of *union* let me remind you of the method of solving quadratic equations by factoring. Suppose we wish to solve

$$x^2 + 7x + 12 = 0.$$

This is equivalent to finding the truth set

$$\{x|x^2 + 7x + 12 = 0\}.$$

From elementary algebra we know that

$$x^2 + 7x + 12 = (x + 3)(x + 4).$$

We also know that, if a product is equal to zero, then at least one of the factors is zero. Hence, if x satisfies $x^2 + 7x + 12 = 0$, it must satisfy at least one of the following: $x + 3 = 0$, or $x + 4 = 0$.

Further, if x satisfies either $x + 3 = 0$ or $x + 4 = 0$, it also satisfies $x^2 + 7x + 12 = 0$. A summary of these two statements is

$$\{x|x^2 + 7x + 12 = 0\} = \{x|x + 3 = 0\} \cup \{x|x + 4 = 0\}.$$

Now $\{x|x + 3 = 0\} = \{-3\}$ and $\{x|x + 4 = 0\} = \{-4\}$. Therefore,

$$\{x|x^2 + 7x + 12 = 0\} = \{-3\} \cup \{-4\} = \{-3, -4\}.$$

A particular use of the concept of *intersection* occurs in finding the "simultaneous solution" of

$$2x + 3y = -1,$$
$$x - y = 2.$$

What we want is an ordered pair (x, y) which is an element of both

$$\{(x, y)|2x + 3y = -1\} \quad \text{and} \quad \{(x, y)|x - y = 2\}.$$

Thus we are in fact looking for the truth set:

$$\{(x, y)|2x + 3y = -1\} \cap \{(x, y)|x - y = 2\}.$$

Geometrically we are seeking the point of intersection of the two lines which are the graphs of the two given equations. The answer is $(1, -1)$, but we shall not enter into the method of finding this solution in this chapter.

9. FUNCTIONS.   When you were in school, a function was generally described as some kind of a formula, such as

$$y = 3x^2 - 2x + 1$$

In the traditional notation $3x^2 - 2x + 1$ was called a "function of x", and the students were taught to write

$$f(x) = 3x^2 - 2x + 1.$$

The symbol $f(x)$ is read "f of x" and means "function of x". This idea was so well impressed on my contemporaries in college that our revered professor of mathematics was nicknamed "f of x", or "Effie" for short. Although no one addressed him by this name, I gather that he was aware of it, for in his will he left money to endow the

"$f(x)$ Scholarship in Mathematics". You can imagine the problem this presented to the administrator of his estate, who was a mathematically illiterate business man.

In contemporary mathematics functions play a much wider role as relationships between two sets. Let us consider the following pairs:

A	B
Real number x	The real number $x^2 - 2x + 7$
A letter	The postage required to send this letter by airmail
A positive real number x	The logarithm of x
A telephone subscriber	His phone number
A college student	His age
A circle	The length of its radius
A town	The dot on a map which represents this town

What is it that is common to these very assorted pairs of numbers, people, objects, etc.? First, the element on the left is a typical member of a well-defined set: the set of real numbers, the set of letters, the set of circles in the plane, etc. This set is called the *domain* of the function we are defining. The element on the right is a member of another set called the *range* of the function. So in each pair two sets are involved, the domain and the range. But there is still more to the idea of a function. In each case in the table there is a procedure which associates a particular element of the range with a chosen element of the domain. I call this the *rule*.

A function, then, has three components:

(1) A set, called the domain.

(2) A set, called the range.

(3) A rule. In applying this rule we choose an element of the domain and are led by the rule to a unique element of the range.

It is also possible to look at functions from a more sophisticated point of view. Let us consider two sets, A and B. We define the Cartesian Product of A and B (written $A \times B$) to be the set of ordered pairs (a, b) where a is an element of A and b is an element of B. Let us direct our interest toward various subsets of $A \times B$. Any such subset is called a *relation*.

For example, consider the case where A and B are each the set of real numbers. Then $A \times B$ is the set of ordered pairs of real numbers. As a subset consider those ordered pairs (a, b) where $b = 2 - a$.

We get an infinite collection of pairs such as $(1, 1)$, $(0, 2)$, $(3, -1)$, $(1\frac{1}{2}, \frac{1}{2})$, etc. The set of all such ordered pairs is the relation so defined.

Another relation is the set of ordered pairs whose elements satisfy the inequality: $a^2 + b^2 < 16$. Particular elements of this set are $(1, 1)$, $(1, 2)$, $(1, 3)$, $(2, 1)$, $(2, 2)$, etc.

These two relations differ in one important respect. In the relation defined by $b = 2 - a$, each value of a determines a unique value of b. Hence this is an example of a function. On the other hand, in the relation defined by $a^2 + b^2 < 16$, there are infinitely many values of b that can be associated with $a = 1$. Indeed any b such that $b^2 < 15$ will work. Thus this relation is *not* an example of a function. So that we may identify those relations which actually are functions, we shall define a function as a special case of a relation.

Definition. *Consider a relation which is a subset of the Cartesian Product $A \times B$. This relation is a function if and only if no two ordered pairs (a, b) which are elements of this relation have the same first element, a.*

From this point of view a function is a set of ordered pairs,

$$\{(a_1, b_1), (a_2, b_2), (a_3, b_3) \ldots\},$$

in which no two a's are the same. There is no such restriction on the b's, which may be equal or different as you wish. The *domain* of the function is the set $\{a_1, a_2, a_3 \ldots\}$. The *range* is the set $\{b_1, b_2, b_3 \ldots\}$. The *rule* is: to each a in the range associate the b with which it is paired above.

PROBLEMS

1. Which of the following sets are identical:
    (a) $\{1, 3, 7, 9\}$; (b) $\{x|x^2 = 4\}$; (c) $\{x|x = 2\}$; (d) $\{-2, 2\}$;
    (e) $\{7, 3, 1, 9\}$; (f) $\{x|5x = 10\}$.
2. Which of the following pairs of sets can be placed in a 1 to 1 correspondence:
    (a) A = the set of nations in the world.
       B = the set of heads of state of the nations in the world.
    (b) $A = \{1, 3, 5, 7\}$; $B = \{1, 3, 5, 9\}$.
    (c) $A = \{1, 3, 5, 7\}$; $B = \{1, 3, 5, 7, 9\}$.

(d) A = the set of married men in the United States.
  B = the set of women in the United States.
(e) A = the set of your children.
  B = the set of PTA's to which you do (or should) belong.
(f) A = the set of problems in this book.
  B = the set of problems in this book which you can solve.

3. Suppose that the universal set U is $\{1, 2, 3, 4, 5, 6, 7, 8, 9, 10\}$. Find the complements of:
  (a) $\{1, 3, 6\}$; (b) $\{4, 7, 8, 9, 10\}$; (c) $\{1, 2, 3, 4, 5, 6, 7, 8, 9, 10\}$.

4. Find the union $(A \cup B)$ and the intersection $(A \cap B)$ of the pairs of sets:
  (a) $A = \{1, 3, 5, 7, 9\}$; $B = \{1, 2, 3\}$.
  (b) A = The set of positive even integers; B = The set of positive odd integers.
  (c) A = the set of boats with sails; B = the set of boats with motors.
  (d) $A = \{x | x^2 - 7x + 12 = 0\}$; $B = \{x | x = 3\}$.

5. Find the truth sets of the following open sentences:
  (a) $2x - 4 = 0$.
  (b) $x^2 - 4x + 4 = 0$.
  (c) $x^2 - 7x + 10 = 0$.
  (d) x was the secretary of state on Jan. 1, 1964.
  (e) x (teams) played in the World Series in 1963.

6. Plot the graph of the set $\{(x, y) | x + y = 1\}$.

7. Write down the sets of ordered pairs that are elements of the function for which:
  The domain is the set of positive integers less than 4.
  The range is the set of positive integers less than 16.
  The rule is: to an integer x in the domain assign the integer x^2 in the range.

8. Write down the sets of ordered pairs that are elements of the function for which:
  The domain is the set of your children.
  The range is the set of their grades last term in mathematics.
  The rule is: to each child assign his grade.

9. Write down three sets of ordered pairs belonging to the relation defined by $x^2 + y^2 < 25$, where x and y are real numbers.

10. State whether the following equations define functions, or only relations. Assume that x and y are real.
  (a) $y = 3x + 5$;   (d) $y = 3x^2 + 7x - 2$;
  (b) $x^2 + y^2 = 1$;   (e) $y^2 = x^2 + 4$.
  (c) $y > 2x + 1$;

ANSWERS

1. (a) and (e); (b) and (d); (c) and (f).
2. (a); (b); not (c); not (d); (e) depends on your situation; (f) hopefully yes, probably no.
3. (a) $\{2, 4, 5, 7, 8, 9, 10\}$; (b) $\{1, 2, 3, 5, 6\}$; (c) the empty set.
4. (a) Union: $\{1, 2, 3, 5, 7, 9\}$; intersection: $\{1, 3\}$.
   (b) Union: the set of positive integers; intersection: the empty set.
   (c) Union: the set of boats with either motors or sails or both; intersection: the set of motor sailers.
   (d) Union: $\{3, 4\}$; intersection $\{3\}$.
5. (a) $\{2\}$; (b) $\{2\}$; (c) $\{2, 5\}$; (d) Dean Rusk; (e) $\{$Dodgers, Yankees$\}$.
6.

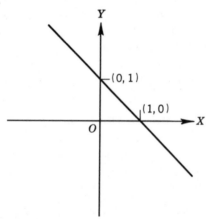

7. $(1, 1)$; $(2, 4)$; $(3, 9)$.
8. Hopefully something like this: (John, A), (James A), (Mary, A), (Margaret, A).
9. $(1, 1)$, $(2, 3)$, $(0, 0)$, and many more.
10. (a) function; (b) not a function; (c) not a function; (d) function; (e) not a function.

CHAPTER 7 THE LAWS OF ALGEBRA

In Chapters 1 and 2, I spoke about the organization of knowledge into a mathematical model, once the facts were known from experience and intuition. In the elementary school the children meet numbers in many situations, and when they reach high school they should be ready to organize what they already know about numbers. In due course they will be able to deal with the operations on numbers in terms of an abstract mathematical system, known as a *field*. They will be able to do this more readily if their intuition and thinking are guided by a teacher who knows the details of the ultimate goal. In this chapter we shall describe the nature of a field, so that you can see where your children are being led in their earlier years. When they are juniors or seniors in high school they will then have no trouble with this abstract system.

I wish to make it clear, however, that I do not advocate the introduction of these laws as axioms until the last year of the high school. In the elementary school and the early years of high school they should be introduced as *summaries* of information which is already known to the children. In this way the youngsters will be helped to organize their mathematical knowledge. Finally, in the senior year, the approach should shift, the laws should become axioms, and the day-to-day algebraic operations should be proved on the basis of these axioms. In this chapter I shall assume that you have seen algebra (at some time or other) and that you are ready for a summary of what you remember, or at least a review of what you once knew.

The easiest way to approach any abstract idea is to start with a concrete illustration of it. So we approach *fields* by examining the algebraic properties of the real number system.

Properties of the Real Numbers

1. CLOSURE.   If you add two real numbers it is evident that the sum is another real number. Similarly, the product of two real numbers is a real number. For this reason we say that the real numbers are closed under addition and multiplication.

This property may seem so trivial that it is not worth stating. But there are familiar systems that are not closed in this way. The sum of two prime numbers is not in general a prime, for $3 + 5 = 8$, which is not a prime. The product of two irrational numbers is not necessarily irrational, for $\sqrt{2} \times \sqrt{8} = \sqrt{16} = 4$, which is rational. The difference of two positive numbers is not necessarily positive, for $3 - 5 = -2$. Thus this closure property of the real numbers describes something about them which is not shared by many other sets of numbers.

2. COMMUTATIVE LAWS.   Another simple property of real numbers is that their addition and multiplication are commutative.. This means that

$$a + b = b + a \qquad \text{and} \qquad a \times b = b \times a.$$

Children learn these in the early grades from actual experience with the addition and multiplication tables, and it may be shocking to visualize algebraic systems in which these laws fail. Perhaps the simplest such example is that of the multiplication of 2×2 matrices.

A 2×2 matrix is a square array of real numbers written in the form

$$\begin{pmatrix} a & b \\ c & d \end{pmatrix}.$$

By definition the product of two such matrices is obtained from the formula

$$\begin{pmatrix} a & b \\ c & d \end{pmatrix} \times \begin{pmatrix} w & x \\ y & z \end{pmatrix} = \begin{pmatrix} aw + by & ax + bz \\ cw + dy & cx + dz \end{pmatrix}.$$

I am sorry that space does not permit me to motivate this definition, but please believe me—there is a good reason for it. If we apply this in a particular case, we get

$$\begin{pmatrix} 1 & 3 \\ -1 & 2 \end{pmatrix} \times \begin{pmatrix} 2 & 1 \\ 0 & -1 \end{pmatrix} = \begin{pmatrix} 2 & -2 \\ -2 & -3 \end{pmatrix},$$

whereas

$$\begin{pmatrix} 2 & 1 \\ 0 & -1 \end{pmatrix} \times \begin{pmatrix} 1 & 3 \\ -1 & 2 \end{pmatrix} = \begin{pmatrix} 1 & 8 \\ 1 & -2 \end{pmatrix}.$$

Since

$$\begin{pmatrix} 2 & -2 \\ -2 & -3 \end{pmatrix} \neq \begin{pmatrix} 1 & 8 \\ 1 & -2 \end{pmatrix},$$

this type of multiplication is not commutative.

3. ASSOCIATIVE LAWS. The addition and multiplication tables tell us how to add or multiply a *pair* of real numbers. But there is nothing in these tables that helps us with the sum $2 + 5 + 9$ or the product $4 \times 6 \times 2$. The sums and products of *triples* of numbers need to be defined, and similar problems occur when we deal with quadruples and larger sets of numbers.

If this matter bothered you when you were in school, you have undoubtedly forgotten about it by now, but the situation is more serious for your young children. What shall we do about $2 + 5 + 9$? There are at least two possibilities. First, you might add 2 to 5 and get 7, and then add 7 to 9 and get 16. We write this as

$$2 + 5 + 9 = (2 + 5) + 9 = 16.$$

On the other hand, you might add 5 to 9 and get 14, and then add 2 to 14 and get 16. We write this as $2 + (5 + 9) = 16$. From this example we observe that

$$(2 + 5) + 9 = 2 + (5 + 9).$$

After some experience we realize that, for every triple of real numbers, a, b, c,

$$(a + b) + c = a + (b + c).$$

This is the *Associative Law* for *Addition*. The parallel law for multiplication is

$$(a \times b) \times c = a \times (b \times c).$$

We must return to the definition of $a + b + c$ and $a \times b \times c$. We have two choices, and because of the associative laws they are equivalent. So we *define*

$$a + b + c = (a + b) + c,$$
$$a \times b \times c = (a \times b) \times c.$$

Now what shall we do about $a + b + c + d$? Since $a + b + c$ and $a \times b \times c$ are already defined, it is legitimate to *define*

$$a + b + c + d = (a + b + c) + d,$$
$$a \times b \times c \times d = (a \times b \times c) \times d.$$

In a similar fashion we proceed step by step to define the sum and product of any finite set of real numbers.

The associative and commutative laws tell us that the sum of a set of numbers is the same regardless of the order in which we perform the operation. Let us prove, for example, that

$$a + b + c = c + b + a.$$

Proof:

$$
\begin{aligned}
a + b + c &= (a + b) + c & \text{(Definition)} \\
&= (b + a) + c & \text{(Commutative Law)} \\
&= c + (b + a) & \text{(Commutative Law)} \\
&= (c + b) + a & \text{(Associative Law)} \\
&= c + b + a. & \text{(Definition)}
\end{aligned}
$$

A similar situation holds for multiplication.

4. IDENTITY ELEMENTS.   In Chapter 5 we remarked that zero has the special property that for all real numbers a

$$a + 0 = 0 + a = a.$$

This is the definition of zero, and all other properties of it must be *proved* in terms of this. Since the addition of zero leaves a identically as it was originally, we call zero the *additive identity element*.

It is now reasonable to ask whether there is a multiplicative identity element, that is, a number such that a times this number is a itself. Of course there is; this number is 1. We observe that for every a

$$a \times 1 = 1 \times a = a$$

and therefore call 1 the multiplicative *identity element*.

5. INVERSE ELEMENTS.   To define such elements we pick an a and ask: Are there numbers x and y such that

$$a + x = x + a = 0, \qquad ay = ya = 1?$$

If $a = 3$, we know the answers, namely, $x = -3$ and $y = \frac{1}{3}$. If $a = -2$, the answers are $x = +2$, $y = -\frac{1}{2}$. If $a = 0$, we have $x = 0$, but there is trouble with y. We want $0 \cdot y = 1$. As we shall see later, $0 \cdot y = 0$ for all y, and so there can be no y with the required property.

From these examples we see that given any real number a there is another real number ^-a such that

$$a + {}^-a = {}^-a + a = 0.$$

The number ^-a is called the *additive inverse* of a. Some people write $-a$ instead of ^-a, but this is confusing for it gives the false impression that ^-a is negative. The sign of ^-a depends upon that of a! For example: $^-(3) = -3; {}^-(-3) = 3, {}^-(0) = 0$.

Moreover, unless $a = 0$, there is another real number a' such that

$$a \times a' = a' \times a = 1.$$

This number a' is called the *multiplicative inverse* of a. For example, $2' = \frac{1}{2}; (\frac{1}{2})' = 2; (-3)' = -\frac{1}{3}$.

In terms of these inverse elements we can define subtraction and division.

Definitions. $(a - b)$ *and* (a/b) *are defined by the equations:*

$$a - b = a + ({}^-b),$$
$$a/b = a \times (b') \quad \text{provided } b \neq 0.$$

There is one more law which we shall only state here. It is the Distributive Law, and its consequences are so numerous that they require the whole of the next chapter.

6. DISTRIBUTIVE LAW.   For every triple of real numbers, a, b, c,

$$a \times (b + c) = (a \times b) + (a \times c).$$

These six laws contain all the necessary information about the algebra of real numbers—apart from their order properties to be discussed in Chapter 9. They therefore form the basis of algebra, and every theorem and rule of algebra is implicit in them.

Fields

Our final step is to construct a mathematical model based upon these as axioms. We define it as follows:

A *field* consists of:

(a) A set, F, of undefined elements, containing at least two distinct elements.

(b) A pair of undefined operations, $+$ and $\times$, called addition and multiplication.

(c) The following set of six axioms:

1. F is closed under $+$ and $\times$.
2. The operations $+$ and $\times$ are associative.
3. The operations $+$ and $\times$ are commutative.
4. There exist additive and multiplicative identity elements, 0 and 1 respectively.
5. Every element of F has an additive inverse, and every element other than zero has a multiplicative inverse.
6. Multiplication is distributive over addition.

Elementary algebra is the subject in which the properties of a field are studied. Let us, then, consider some of the consequences of these axioms as they apply to elementary algebra. That is, we shall prove three theorems based on the above axioms.

Theorem 1. $-(-a) = a$.

Proof:

1. $-(-a) + (-a) = 0$.   (Axiom 5)

    Now add a to both sides. You get:

2. $[-(-a) + (-a)] + a = 0 + a$,

or

3. $-(-a) + [(-a) + a] = a$.   (Axioms 2 and 4)
4. $-(-a) + 0 = a$.   (Axiom 5)
5. $-(-a) = a$.   (Axiom 4)

Theorem 2. $-(a + b) = (^-a) + (^-b)$.

Proof:
1. $^-(a + b) + (a + b) = 0$.   (Axiom 5)
     Add $(^-a) + (^-b)$ to each side:
2. $[^-(a + b) + (a + b)] + [(^-a) + (^-b)] = 0 + [(^-a) + (^-b)]$.
3. $^-(a + b) + [(a + b) + (^-a) + (^-b)] = (^-a) + (^-b)$.
                                                        (Axioms 2 and 4)
4. $^-(a + b) + 0 = (^-a) + (^-b)$.   (Axioms 2–5)
5. $^-(a + b) = (^-a) + (^-b)$.   (Axiom 4)

Theorem 3.   *Let a and b be any two elements of F. Then there exists a unique element of F, x, such that*

$$a + x = b.$$

This theorem has two parts: existence and unicity of x.

Proof of existence: $x = b - a$ has the required property, for:
1. $a + (b - a) = a + [b + (^-a)]$ (Definition of subtraction)
2. $= a + [(^-a) + b]$ (Axiom 3)
3. $= [a + (-a)] + b$ (Axiom 2)
4. $= 0 + b$ (Axiom 5)
5. $= b$.   (Axiom 4)

Proof of unicity: Suppose there are two such x which are unequal; that is, suppose that:
1. $a + x_1 = b$.
2. $a + x_2 = b$.
3. $x_1 \neq x_2$.
     Then from 1 and 2 it follows that
4. $a + x_1 = a + x_2$.
     Add ^-a to each side; the result is:
5. $^-a + [a + x_1] = ^-a + [a + x_2]$,
or
6. $[(^-a) + a] + x_1 = [(^-a) + a] + x_2$.   (Axiom 2)
7. $0 + x_1 = 0 + x_2$.   (Axiom 5)
8. $x_1 = x_2$.   (Axiom 4)

Step 8, however, contradicts step 3. This means that the assumptions 1, 2, and 3 cannot all be true and hence that there is only one x with the required property.

This proof of unicity is an example of an *indirect proof*. I shall discuss this type of reasoning in Chapter 13. If you are confused about it, it would be a good idea to turn there now.

There are quite a few more theorems of this type, but these should be enough to whet your appetite (or do you in!).

Examples of Fields

I have already described how the real numbers form a field, and you may properly ask: Are there other number systems which are also examples of fields? Yes, indeed. There are just lots and lots of fields lying around in mathematics. Two of the most familiar are the fields of rational numbers and of complex numbers. But these behave so much like real numbers that they are not particularly worth looking at here. I should prefer to show you some fields that are quite different from any that would easily occur to you. These are called *finite fields* or *modular fields*.

As an introduction to such matters let me ask you the question:

"If it is now 9 o'clock, what time will it be seven hours from now?" I hope you give the correct answer, "4 o'clock", but the important question is "How did you do the problem?" One systematic way of handling such questions is to add 7 to 9 and then subtract 12: $7 + 9 - 12 = 4$. Try this method to answer the question:

"If it is now 3 o'clock, what time will it be fifteen hours from now?" Answer "6 o'clock". A slightly harder question is:

"If it is now 5 o'clock, what time will it be thirty hours from now?" To solve this we compute $5 + 30 - 2(12) = 11$ o'clock.

In this way we can construct a new kind of addition which is the same as ordinary addition, except that from the ordinary answer we subtract that multiple of twelve which will leave a remainder between 0 and 11 inclusive. Arithmetic of this kind is called *modular arithmetic*, the *modulus* in this example being 12.

I chose 12 as an example because of its practical use in figuring time, but it is too complicated for the rest of what I wish to do. Let me then carry on from here using 5 as a modulus. To see how to add in this system, let me write down the addition table.

ADDITION TABLE, MODULUS 5

+	0	1	2	3	4
0	0	1	2	3	4
1	1	2	3	4	0
2	2	3	4	0	1
3	3	4	0	1	2
4	4	0	1	2	3

The entry $2 + 4$ in this table, for example, is obtained by the computation: $2 + 4 - 5 = 1$. Note that there is no point in extending the table to numbers such as 6, 10, 22; for these are the same as 1, 0, and 2 from this point of view.

Let us see what properties of addition we can observe in this system. First, you can check to make sure that this addition satisfies those of the axioms of a field that refer to addition. Let us try a few samples:

(1) The sum of any pair of numbers chosen from the set $\{0, 1, 2, 3, 4\}$ is another number in this set. Hence addition is *closed*.

(2) To test the associative law is tedious; let us check a few cases:

$$2 + (3 + 4) = 2 + 2 = 4, \qquad (2 + 3) + 4 = 0 + 4 = 4,$$
$$1 + (4 + 2) = 1 + 1 = 2, \qquad (1 + 4) + 2 = 0 + 2 = 2.$$

Others work the same way.

(3) The commutative law certainly holds, for

$$2 + 3 = 0, \qquad 3 + 2 = 0,$$

and so forth. Indeed, the whole table is symmetrical about the diagonal running from upper left to lower right.

(4) From the first line it follows that, for any a,

$$0 + a = a.$$

(5) The additive inverses can be computed from the table. They are:

$$^{-}0 = 0; \quad ^{-}1 = 4; \quad ^{-}2 = 3; \quad ^{-}3 = 2, \quad ^{-}4 = 1;$$

for they must satisfy $a + (^-a) = 0$, or

$$0 + 0 = 0; \quad 1 + 4 = 0; \quad 2 + 3 = 0; \quad 3 + 2 = 0; \quad 4 + 1 = 0.$$

These facts enable us to solve equations of the form

$$a + x = b$$

in this number system, for Theorem 3 assures us that this is possible.
Consider the equation

$$3 + x = 1.$$

If we were working in the field of real numbers, it would be a correct
procedure to subtract 3 from each side and obtain $x = -2$. In this
system, however, there are no negative numbers, and so it is best to
return to first principles. To remove 3 from the left side, the thing to
do is to add $^-3$ to both sides. This gives

$$^-3 + (3 + x) = \,^-3 + 1.$$

But we saw that $^-3 = 2$, so this is

$$2 + (3 + x) = 2 + 1,$$

or

$$(2 + 3) + x = 3,$$

or

$$0 + x = 3,$$

or

$$x = 3.$$

In solving a problem of this kind, you can really get to the
essentials of elementary algebra, and do not need to rely upon ill-
understood short cuts such as "move 3 to the right side and change
its sign". In this way problems in modular arithmetic help you to
understand ordinary algebra, for they show you how things work in
a general field and hence in the field of real numbers.

To complicate matters, it is amusing to write down the multiplication table in this system.

MULTIPLICATION TABLE, MODULUS 5

×	0	1	2	3	4
0	0	0	0	0	0
1	0	1	2	3	4
2	0	2	4	1	3
3	0	3	1	4	2
4	0	4	3	2	1

As before we can check to see that this kind of arithmetic satisfies the multiplicative properties of a field. The only complicated part is finding the multiplicative inverses. They are

$$1' = 1; \quad 2' = 3; \quad 3' = 2; \quad 4' = 4.$$

Notice that 0 has no multiplicative inverse.

Now we can solve more complicated equations such as

$$3x + 4 = 3.$$

First add $^-4$ (which equals 1) to both sides. The result is

$$(3x + 4) + 1 = 3 + 1,$$

or

$$3x + (4 + 1) = 4,$$

or

$$3x = 4.$$

In ordinary algebra you would now divide by 3 and get $x = \frac{4}{3}$; but here this is nonsense since $\frac{4}{3}$ is not one of our numbers. Instead we multiply both sides by $3' = 2$:

$$(2 \cdot 3)x = 2 \cdot 4,$$

or

$$1 \cdot x = 3,$$

or

$$x = 3.$$

If, finally, we check the distributive law, we see that the integers with modulus 5 satisfy all the axioms of a field. Thus there are some, strange looking "fields".

You may indeed wonder if there are any familiar systems of numbers which are not fields. By all means! The positive integers:

1, 2, 3, 4, . . . do not form a field, for there is no additive identity and there are neither additive nor multiplicative inverses. Neither does the set of all integers,

$$\{\cdot\ \cdot\ \cdot\ -4,\ -3,\ -2,\ -1,\ 0,\ 1,\ 2,\ 3,\ 4,\ \ldots\},$$

for there are no multiplicative inverses.

Since, however, fields constitute those number systems in which your old familiar algebra still works, they are the major objects of study in school algebra.

PROBLEMS

1. Prove: $(a')' = a$.
2. Prove: $(ab)' = a'b'$.
3. Prove: There exists one and only one solution of the equation

$$ax = b \qquad \text{where} \qquad a \neq 0.$$

4. Prove: There exists one and only one solution of the equation

$$ax + b = c \qquad \text{where} \qquad a \neq 0.$$

5. Prove: $\dfrac{(a/b)}{(c/d)} = \dfrac{ad}{ac}$ where $b \neq 0,\ c \neq 0,\ d \neq 0.$

6. In the number field with modulus 5, solve:
   (a) $4 + x = 2$;   (d) $3x + 2 = 4$;
   (b) $3 + x = 1$;   (e) $2x + 3 = 1$;
   (c) $2 + x = 4$;   (f) $4x + 4 = 2$.

7. Write the addition and multiplication tables for modulus 4. Do these satisfy the axioms of a field?

8. In the number system with modulus 4, can you solve the equation:

$$2x + 3 = 2?$$

9. Show that the number system with modulus 3 is a field.

10. (Hard)   For which moduli do the corresponding number systems form a field?

ANSWERS

1. Imitate the proof of Theorem 1.
2. Imitate the proof of Theorem 2.
3. Imitate the proof of Theorem 3.

4. A solution is: $x = \dfrac{c - b}{a}$. To prove this is unique, suppose there are two different solutions x_1 and x_2 with $x_1 \neq x_2$. Then

$$ax_1 + b = ax_2 + b,$$
$$ax_1 = ax_2,$$
$$a'(ax_1) = a'(ax_2),$$
$$(a' \cdot a)x_1 = (a' \cdot a)x_2,$$
$$1 \cdot x_1 = 1 \cdot x_2,$$
$$x_1 = x_2,$$

which is a contradiction.

5. $\dfrac{(a/b)}{(c/d)} = \dfrac{ab'}{cd'} = (ab') \cdot (cd')' = (ab') \cdot (c'd) = (ad)(b'c') = (ad)(bc)' = ad/bc$. Give reasons for each step.

6. (a) 3;   (d) 4;
   (b) 3;   (e) 4;
   (c) 2;   (f) 2.

7.

+	0	1	2	3
0	0	1	2	3
1	1	2	3	0
2	2	3	0	1
3	3	0	1	2

×	0	1	2	3
0	0	0	0	0
1	0	1	2	3
2	0	2	0	2
3	0	3	2	1

No. 2 does not have a multiplicative inverse.

8. No. There is no solution since $2'$ does not exist.

9. Write the addition and multiplication tables. They are

+	0	1	2
0	0	1	2
1	1	2	0
2	2	0	1

×	0	1	2
0	0	0	0
1	0	1	2
2	0	2	1

Now check the axioms:

$$^-0 = 0, \ ^-1 = 2, \ ^-2 = 1; \qquad 1' = 1, \ 2' = 2.$$

10. The modulus must be a prime, that is, a number with no divisors other than itself and one.

CHAPTER 8 THE DISTRIBUTIVE LAW

I have saved the *Distributive Law* for a chapter of its own because of its very great importance. Something like one-half of the manipulations of algebra depend upon this law, and much of the trouble students have with algebra results from their ignorance of it.

The essential idea behind this law is that it establishes a connection between multiplication and addition. You will observe that all the other laws deal separately with these two operations, so that without the distributive law much that is familiar could not be established.

The intuitive idea behind this law is that for positive integers multiplication is repeated addition. For example,

$$3 \times 4 = 3 + 3 + 3 + 3$$
$$= 4 + 4 + 4.$$

Notice that this definition of multiplication does not make sense in other cases such as $\frac{1}{2} \times \frac{3}{4}$, for how can we multiply $\frac{3}{4}$ by itself one-half time? There are similar difficulties with $(-2) \times (-6)$, and these make algebra incomprehensible to a student who has been assured that multiplication is nothing but repeated addition.

To avoid all these troubles, we rely upon the distributive law, which states that, for any triple of real numbers a, b, and c,

$$a \times (b + c) = (a \times b) + (a \times c).$$

Since multiplication is commutative, an equivalent formulation is

$$(b + c) \times a = (b \times a) + (c \times a).$$

The law is easily extended to sums with more terms, such as

$$a \times (b + c + d) = (a \times b) + (a \times c) + (a \times d).$$

I can give many easy applications of this law. First let me apply it to positive integers, and use it to show that, for these, multiplication is in fact repeated addition. I assume that it has already been established, for instance, that

$$4 = 1 + 1 + 1 + 1.$$

Then

$$3 \times 4 = 3 \times (1 + 1 + 1 + 1)$$
$$= 3 + 3 + 3 + 3$$

by the distributive law. In other words, 3 times 4 is the sum of four three's. Similarly,

$$3 = 1 + 1 + 1,$$
$$4 \times 3 = 4 \times [1 + 1 + 1],$$
$$= 4 + 4 + 4,$$

or 4 times 3 is the sum of three four's.

To make the situation doubly clear, I remind you that there are two statements to be considered:

(1) The Distributive Law.

(2) Multiplication is Repeated Addition.

For positive integers these two are equivalent. For various other types of products, however, (2) is meaningless whereas (1) continues to make sense. It is, therefore, wise to use (1) in all circumstances and to de-emphasize (2).

As another illustration of the use of the distributive law,

consider

$$2 \times (4 + 7) = (2 \times 4) + (2 \times 7)$$
$$= 8 + 14$$
$$= 22.$$

The usual method of long multiplication is based on this law, for

$$24 \times 56 = 24 \times (50 + 6)$$
$$= (24 \times 50) + (24 \times 6)$$
$$= 1200 + 144$$
$$= 1344.$$

We usually write this in the form

	24		24
	×56	or	×56
	144		144
	1200		120
	1344		1344

Less well understood is the use of this law from right to left in the process of factoring. That is,

$$(a \times b) + (a \times c) = a \times (b + c).$$

In numbers, we can therefore write

$$35 + 75 = (5 \times 7) + (5 \times 15)$$
$$= 5 \times (7 + 15)$$
$$= 5 \times 22$$
$$= 110.$$

The law is also responsible for a number of short-cut methods in arithmetic which periodically attract a substantial following. Thus:

$$523 \times 9 = 523 \times (10 - 1)$$
$$= 5230 - 523$$
$$= 4707,$$
$$32 \times 16 = (30 + 2) \times 16$$
$$= 480 + 32$$
$$= 512.$$

The idea is to do most of the steps mentally, and to write down only the answer.

The distributive law is observed to hold for positive integers, but there is no way of testing its validity for situations where any of a, b, or c is zero, negative, or fractional. Since such numbers are creatures of our own minds we are free to give them any properties we wish. Because the distributive law is so useful for positive integers, we assume that it is to be true for all real numbers. This assumption has several very important consequences.

First, let us prove that for any real number a

$$a \times 0 = 0.$$

You doubtless believe this already, and wonder what the point of this is. Remember that zero is defined by its properties of *addition* ($a + 0 = a$) and that nothing was said about multiplication. You cannot go from addition to multiplication without consulting the distributive law. So why is $a \times 0 = 0$?

Well:

$$0 + 0 = 0,$$
$$a \times (0 + 0) = a \times 0,$$
$$(a \times 0) + (a \times 0) = a \times 0, \qquad \text{(Distributive law)}$$
$$a \times 0 = 0. \qquad \text{(Adding } -(a \times 0) \text{ to each side)}$$

This simple proof is typical of the power of this law.

To give another illustration, let us compute the value of $4 \times (-3)$, supposing that no one ever told us how to multiply signed numbers. Notice that we are now abandoning the earlier notation $^-3$ and are using the more conventional -3, the former notation having served its purpose. We start with

$$3 + (-3) = 0, \qquad \text{(Definition of } -3)$$
$$4 \times [3 + (-3)] = 4 \times 0,$$
$$(4 \times 3) + [4 \times (-3)] = 0, \qquad \text{(Distributive law)}$$
$$12 + [4 \times (-3)] = 0.$$

On the other hand

$$12 + (-12) = 0. \qquad \text{(Definition of } -12)$$

So

$$12 + [4 \times (-3)] = 12 + (-12),$$

or

$$4 \times (-3) = -12.$$

Thus we see that a positive number times a negative number is negative without having to rely upon some arbitrary rule handed down by the teacher as something to be memorized or else!

Can you prove now that $(-3) \times (-4) = 12$? I leave the problem to you, but suggest that you start with

$$4 + (-4) = 0.$$

Other formulas of algebra can be obtained by using this law several times over. For example,

$$
\begin{aligned}
(a + b)^2 &= (a + b) \times (a + b) \\
&= [(a + b) \times a] + [(a + b) \times b] \\
&= (a^2 + ba) + (ab + b^2) \\
&= a^2 + ba + ab + b^2 \\
&= a^2 + 2ab + b^2.
\end{aligned}
$$

Also

$$(a + b) \times (c + d) = ac + ad + bc + bd. \quad \text{(Prove it!)}$$

Thus

$$
\begin{aligned}
18 \times 12 &= (20 - 2) \times (10 + 2) \\
&= 200 - 20 + 40 - 4 \\
&= 240 - 24 \\
&= 216.
\end{aligned}
$$

Some misconceptions regarding division are also susceptible to therapy by means of this law:

$$
\begin{aligned}
\frac{2x + 5}{2} &= \frac{1}{2}(2x + 5) \\
&= (\tfrac{1}{2})(2x) + (\tfrac{1}{2})(5) \\
&= x + (\tfrac{5}{2}).
\end{aligned}
$$

Students have been known to think that the correct answer is $x + 5$; they have merely cancelled the 2's.

Using this idea we can see why it is true that an integer is divisible by 3 if the sum of its decimal digits is divisible by 3. An example makes this clear.

$$\begin{aligned}
\tfrac{258}{3} &= \tfrac{1}{3}[(2 \times 10^2) + (5 \times 10) + 8] \\
&= [2 \times (\tfrac{100}{3})] + [5 \times (\tfrac{10}{3})] + \tfrac{8}{3} \\
&= [2 \times (33 + \tfrac{1}{3})] + [5 \times (3 + \tfrac{1}{3})] + \tfrac{8}{3} \\
&= [(2 \times 33) + 5 \times 3)] + (\tfrac{2}{3} + \tfrac{5}{3} + \tfrac{8}{3}) \\
&= [(2 \times 33) + (5 \times 3)] + \frac{2 + 5 + 8}{3}.
\end{aligned}$$

The answer is thus an integer if and only if $2 + 5 + 8$ is divisible by 3, as it is in this case.

In a similar fashion it is possible to prove that an integer is divisible by 9 if and only if the sum of its digits is divisible by 9. Let me illustrate such a proof:

$$\begin{aligned}
\tfrac{468}{9} &= \tfrac{1}{9}[(4 \times 10^2) + (6 \times 10) + 8] \\
&= (4 \times \tfrac{100}{9}) + (6 \times \tfrac{10}{9}) + \tfrac{8}{9} \\
&= [4 \times (11 + \tfrac{1}{9})] + [6 \times (1 + \tfrac{1}{9})] + \tfrac{8}{9} \\
&= [(4 \times 11) + (6 \times 1)] + (\tfrac{4}{9} + \tfrac{6}{9} + \tfrac{8}{9}) \\
&= [(4 \times 11) + (6 \times 1)] + \frac{4 + 6 + 8}{9}.
\end{aligned}$$

Since $4 + 6 + 8 = 18$, which equals 9×2, the result is an integer and 468 is divisible by 9.

Less well known is a rule for determining whether an integer is divisible by 11. From an example let us try to guess the general situation. Consider

$$\begin{aligned}
\tfrac{396}{11} &= \tfrac{1}{11}[(3 \times 10^2) + (9 \times 10) + 6] \\
&= (3 \times \tfrac{100}{11}) + (9 \times \tfrac{10}{11}) + \tfrac{6}{11} \\
&= [3 \times (9 + \tfrac{1}{11})] + [9 \times (1 - \tfrac{1}{11})] + \tfrac{6}{11} \\
&= [(3 \times 9) + (9 \times 1)] + \frac{3 - 9 + 6}{11}.
\end{aligned}$$

Since $\dfrac{3 - 9 + 6}{11}$ is an integer (actually it is zero), 396 is divisible by 11.

What, then, is the general rule? It is "An integer is divisible by eleven if and only if the sum of its number of units, minus its number of tens, plus its number of hundreds, minus its number of thousands, etc., is divisible by 11".

For example, 4829 is divisible by 11, for $-4 + 8 - 2 + 9 = 11$, which is divisible by 11.

The only trouble with the distributive law is that some students learn it so well that they try to apply it where it does not belong. Some of them think that

$$(a + b)^2 = a^2 + b^2,$$

which would imply some kind of distributive law for exponents. There is no such law, since $(2 + 3)^2 = 25$, whereas $2^2 + 3^2 = 14$. The only distributive law is the one we have given, and this refers to addition and multiplication alone!

This concludes the properties of a field. Remember that they were obtained by intuition from the observed properties of numbers, and that my only role here has been to organize what you already knew. This is what I meant in Chapter 1 by the construction of a mathematical model. Now that you have seen one, I hope that you will not feel that mathematical abstractions are beyond you.

The next step in algebra is to assume these laws as axioms and to prove as many interesting theorems as possible. This will be the program for your high school son or daughter, and if you begin with these axioms you will see that algebra need not be a stranger to anyone.

PROBLEMS

1. Apply the distributive law to remove the parentheses in the following expressions:
   (a) $2(7 + 5)$ (d) $3(2x + y)$
   (b) $(-3)[4 + (-2)]$ (e) $2x(x^2 - 1)$
   (c) $(-4)(5 - 3)$ (f) $3x(2x^2 + x - 4)$

2. Apply the distributive law (right to left) to "remove a common factor" from the following expressions:
   (a) $2 + 6$ (d) $3x^2 + x$
   (b) $-5 + 10$ (e) $2x^3 - 4x + 6$
   (c) $2x + 4y$ (f) $4x^2 + 8x$

3. Use the distributive law to show that
   (a) $(-4) \times 3 = (-4) + (-4) + (-4)$.
   (b) $(-1) \times 5 = (-1) + (-1) + (-1) + (-1) + (-1)$.

4. Use the distributive law to provide a short-cut method of multiplying the following:
   (a) 64×9 (*Hint:* Try $64(10 - 1)$)   (c) 176×99
   (b) 52×11 (d) 256×101

5. Prove that $(-3)(-4) = 12$.

6. Prove that $a \times (-b) = -ab$.

7. Prove that $(-a) \times (-b) = ab$.

8. Which of the following numbers (base ten) are divisible by 9? (a) 7351; (b) 4257; (c) 54,325.

9. Which of the following numbers (base ten) are divisible by 11? (a) 6831; (b) 5872; (c) 496,397.

10. Prove the following test for divisibility by 7: "Write the given number as a numeral to base 7. Then it is divisible by seven if and only if the last digit in this numeral is a zero." Apply this test to 1218_{ten}.

ANSWERS

1. (a) $14 + 10$ (d) $6x + 3y$
   (b) $-12 + 6$ (e) $2x^3 - 2x$
   (c) $-20 + 12$ (f) $6x^3 + 3x^2 - 12x$

2. (a) $2(1 + 3)$ (d) $x(3x + 1)$
   (b) $5(-1 + 2)$ or $(-5)(1 - 2)$ (e) $2(x^3 - 2x + 3)$
   (c) $2(x + 2y)$ (f) $4x(x + 2)$

3. (a) $(-4) \times 3 = (-4) \times (1 + 1 + 1) = (-4) + (-4) + (-4)$;
   (b) $(-1) \times 5 = (-1) \times (1 + 1 + 1 + 1 + 1)$,
   $= (-1) + (-1) + (-1) + (-1) + (-1)$.

4. (a) $64(10 - 1) = 640 - 64 = 576$.
   (b) $52(10 + 1) = 520 + 52 = 572$.
   (c) $176(100 - 1) = 17600 - 176 = 17,424$.
   (d) $256(100 + 1) = 25600 + 256 = 25,856$.

5. As suggested in the text, start with:

$$4 + (-4) = 0,$$
$$(-3)[4 + (-4)] = (-3) \times 0,$$
$$[(-3) \times 4] + [(-3) \times (-4)] = 0,$$
$$-12 + [(-3) \times (-4)] = 0,$$
$$12 + (-12) + [(-3) \times (-4)] = 12 + 0,$$
$$(-3) \times (-4) = 12.$$

6.
$$b + (-b) = 0,$$
$$a[b + (-b)] = a \times 0 = 0,$$
$$-ab + ab + [a \times (-b)] = -ab + 0,$$
$$a \times (-b) = -ab.$$

7.
$$a + (-a) = 0,$$
$$[a + (-a)] \times (-b) = 0 \times (-b),$$
$$a(-b) + [(-a) \times (-b)] = 0.$$

From Prob. 6, $a(-b) = -ab$, so
$$-ab + [(-a) \times (-b)] = 0,$$
$$ab - ab + [(-a) \times (-b)] = ab + 0,$$
$$(-a) \times (-b) = ab.$$

8. Only (b).

9. (a) and (c).

10. If a number has a representation to base seven with 0 as the last digit, it is of the form:

$$(a \times 7^4) + (b \times 7^3) + (c \times 7^2) + (d \times 7) + 0,$$

which is certainly divisible by 7. Yes, 1218_{ten} is divisible by 7, for it equals 3360_{seven}.

CHAPTER 9 INEQUALITIES

In spite of the Declaration of Independence and its assertion that "all men are created equal", inequality plays a fundamental role in our lives. Youngsters take pride in being older than their friends; oldsters point out that others are older than they are. Businessmen compare this year's profits with last year's, and the study of comparative scores is a favorite pastime during football season. Since so much of our lives is concerned with inequalities, it is surprising that they have played so minor a role in mathematics instruction. Modern courses in algebra, however, have raised them to the same level of importance as equalities. Since inequalities are probably new to you, I must discuss them from the beginning.

Throughout this chapter we shall understand that all numbers mentioned are real numbers. From our knowledge of the real numbers we are aware that they subdivide into three subsets:

(1) The positive real numbers,
(2) The negative real numbers,
(3) Zero, which is neither positive nor negative.

Moreover, each number belongs in one and only one of these subsets. This means, for instance, that no number is simultaneously positive and negative.

This observation permits me to define inequality as follows:

Definition.   *For two real numbers a and b, the statement $a > b$ (read "a is greater than b") is equivalent to the statement $a - b$ is positive. Similarly, $a < b$ (read "a is less than b") is equivalent to the statement $a - b$ is negative.*

We can interpret this geometrically as follows. Arrange the real numbers on the number line in the usual way with positive numbers to the right and negative numbers to the left. Then "greater than" means "to the right of" and "less than" means "to the left of".

Since $a - b$ is either positive, zero, or negative, we can conclude that: *Given any two real numbers a and b, precisely one of the following is true:*

$$a > b, \qquad a = b, \qquad a < b.$$

This statement is called the *Law of Trichotomy*.

We also recall several other properties of real numbers:

(1) If a and b are positive, then $a + b$ is positive.
(2) If a and b are positive, then $a \times b$ is positive.
(3) If a is positive and b is negative, then $a \times b$ is negative.
(4) a is positive if and only if $-a$ is negative.

From property (4) it follows that, if $a > b$, then $b < a$. For, if $a - b$ is positive, property (4) tells us that $b - a$ is negative. In the following series of theorems we shall, therefore, consider only the "greater than" statements. You can easily convert these to "less than" statements if you find this necessary. Although there are many theorems about inequalities, I shall give only those that are most common in applications.

Basic Theorems

Theorem 1.   *a is positive if and only if $a > 0$.*

Proof: This is exceedingly simple. For, by definition, $a > 0$ is equivalent to the statement that $a - 0$ is positive, or to the statement that a is positive.

Theorem 2. *a is negative if and only if a < 0.*

The proof is just like that of Theorem 1.

Theorem 3. *If a > b, then a + c > b + c.*

Proof: We want to prove that $a + c > b + c$. From our definition of inequality this is equivalent to proving that $(a + c) - (b + c)$ is positive. To do this, let us have a look:

$$(a + c) - (b + c) = a - b.$$

From our hypothesis $a > b$, that is, $a - b$ is positive. Hence our proof is completed.

Notice the strategy of this proof. We convert the inequality in the conclusion into a statement that "something" is positive. We then examine this "something" and use our hypothesis and simple algebra to show that it is, indeed, positive. This method will work for our other theorems.

Theorem 4. *If a > b and c > d, then a + c > b + d.*

Proof: Examine the sign of

$$(a + c) - (b + d) = (a - b) + (c - d).$$

Since by hypothesis $a - b$ and $c - d$ are both positive, $[(a + c) - (b + d)]$ is positive and the proof is complete.

Theorem 5. *If a > b and c is positive, then ac > bc.*

Proof: Examine $ac - bc = c(a - b)$. Since both factors are positive, the product is positive.

Theorem 6. *If a > b and c is negative, then ac < bc.*

Proof: Examine $ac - bc = c(a - b)$. Since c is negative and $(a - b)$ is positive, the product is negative.

Remark. Theorems 5 and 6 together tell us what happens when we multiply both sides of an inequality by the same number. If this multiplier is positive, we leave the inequality sign ($>$) as it was originally. But if the multiplier is negative, we must replace $>$ by $<$ or $<$ by $>$, that is, we "reverse the inequality." Failure to remember this is the most common source of error in handling inequalities.

Theorem 7.   *If $a > 0$, then $(1/a) > 0$.*

Proof: $1/a = (1/a)^2 \times a$. Since $(1/a)^2$ and a are both positive, so is $1/a$.

Theorem 8.   *If $a^2 > b^2$ and $a > 0$ and $b > 0$, then $a > b$.*

Proof: $a - b = \dfrac{a^2 - b^2}{a + b}$. By hypothesis $(a^2 - b^2)$ and $(a + b)$ are positive. Hence $(a - b)$ is positive.

Theorem 9.   *If $a > b$ and $b > c$, then $a > c$.*

Proof: $a - c = (a - b) + (b - c)$, and both terms on the right are positive by hypothesis.

This theorem is called the *Transitive Law for Inequalities*. Notice that it does not work for football scores!

Applications

Let us now apply these theorems to some typical kinds of problems. First let us look at the inequality

$$3x + 4 > 1.$$

It is hardly appropriate to ask a student to "solve" this, for a "solution" implies a fixed answer, and the answer here is of another type. What we really want is the "truth set" or "solution set":

$$\{x | 3x + 4 > 1\}.$$

Since this set contains infinitely many numbers, the best thing to do is to graph it. First, however, we should simplify matters as best we can. From

$$3x + 4 > 1,$$

we infer

$$3x > 1 - 4, \quad \text{(Theorem 4, adding } -4 \text{ to each side)}$$

or

$$3x > -3,$$

or

$$x > -1. \quad \text{(Theorem 5, multiplying both sides by } \tfrac{1}{3})$$

The graph is given in Fig. 10. The open circle above -1 indicates that -1 is not to be included in the shaded region.

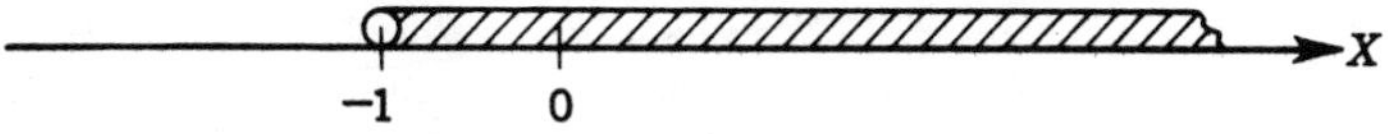

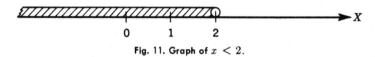

Fig. 10. Graph of $x > -1$.

As another illustration, consider

$$2x + 5 > 4x + 1.$$

This is equivalent to

$$-2x > -4,$$

or to

$$2x < 4,$$

or

$$x < 2.$$

The graph is shown in Fig. 11.

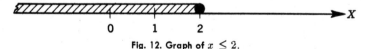

Fig. 11. Graph of $x < 2$.

It is sometimes desirable to introduce the notations $\geq$ and $\leq$ which mean "greater than or equal to" and "less than or equal to" respectively. The graph of $x \leq 2$ is given in Fig. 12 where the circle above 2 is now filled in to indicate that 2 is included in the graph.

Fig. 12. Graph of $x \leq 2$.

Quadratic inequalities are handled in much the same manner. Let us consider

$$x^2 - 4x + 2 > x - 4.$$

This is equivalent to

$$x^2 - 5x + 6 > 0,$$

or to

$$(x - 2)(x - 3) > 0.$$

In order to plot the graph of the solution set of this inequality, I need to explain a further important idea. Let us consider the sign of a quadratic expression $ax^2 + bx + c$ as x moves along the X-axis from left to right. For some values of x the expression may be positive and for others negative. Suppose it is positive at $x = r$ and negative at $x = s$. Then somewhere between r and s the value of $ax^2 + bx + c$ must be zero. In fact, the only way $ax^2 + bx + c$ can change sign is for it to pass through zero. This remark suggests that we examine the values of x for which it is zero, for these are the places where something interesting may happen.

In this problem, $(x - 2)(x - 3)$ is zero at $x = 2$ and $x = 3$. These divide the X-axis into three intervals: $(-\infty, 2)$, $(2, 3)$, $(3, +\infty)$, as shown in Fig. 13. We have just seen that the quadratic

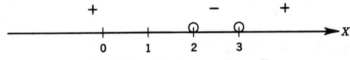

Fig. 13. Sign pattern for $(x - 2)(x - 3)$.

expression $x^2 - 5x + 6 = (x - 2)(x - 3)$ has a constant sign in each interval, so we can find this sign by testing suitable values. In $(-\infty, 2)$, try $x = 0$. At $x = 0$, $(x - 2)(x - 3) = 6$, so our quadratic is positive in this interval. In $(2, 3)$ try $x = 2\frac{1}{2}$. At $x = 2\frac{1}{2}$, $(x - 2)(x - 3) = (\frac{1}{2})(-\frac{1}{2}) = -\frac{1}{4}$, so our quadratic is negative in this interval. Finally, in $(3, +\infty)$, try $x = 4$. At $x = 4$, $(x - 2)(x - 3) = 2$, so our quadratic is positive there. The left and right hand intervals have the required sign, so the graph is as shown in Fig. 14.

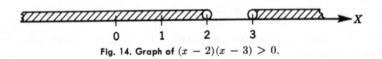

Fig. 14. Graph of $(x - 2)(x - 3) > 0$.

This process depended upon our ability to factor the given quadratic. If we are unable to do so by elementary means, we can rely on the quadratic formula. This says that the roots of

$$ax^2 + bx + c = 0$$

are

$$x = \frac{-b \pm \sqrt{b^2 - 4ac}}{2a}.$$

This gives two values of x which are real if $b^2 - 4ac \geq 0$, but which are not real otherwise. Thus when $b^2 - 4ac \geq 0$, the process shown will solve our problem.

What if, on the other hand, $b^2 - 4ac < 0$? Then $ax^2 + bx + c$ is not zero for any real x. Hence it cannot change sign as x moves from $-\infty$ to $+\infty$, that is, it is definitely positive for all x or negative for all x. Let us try an example:

Find the solution set of $x^2 + x + 1 > 0$. Since $b^2 - 4ac = 1 - 4 = -3$, we know that $x^2 + x + 1$ is either positive or negative for all x. To find out which it is, try $x = 0$. At $x = 0$, $x^2 + x + 1 = 1$, so $x^2 + x + 1$ is positive for all x. The solution set is the entire X-axis.

If, however, our problem had been to find the solution set of $x^2 + x + 1 < 0$, our answer would have been "The empty set."

A frequent use of inequalities involves the notion of *absolute value*. By the absolute value of a real number we mean the distance of the number from 0, taken positively along the number line. The symbol $|a|$ is used to denote the absolute value of a. For example

$$|3| = 3, \qquad |-4| = 4, \qquad |0| = 0.$$

Now what do we mean by stating that $|x| < 4$? This says that the distance of x from 0 is less than 4, or that x is between -4 and $+4$. A convenient notation for this is

$$-4 < x < 4.$$

Similarly,

$$|x + 2| < 6$$

is equivalent to

$$-6 < x + 2 < 6$$

or to

$$-8 < x < 4.$$

Finally,

$$|x - a| < b$$

is equivalent to

$$-b < x - a < b,$$

or

$$a - b < x < a + b.$$

Sometimes the inequality goes the other way, so that we are interested in

$$|x| > 4.$$

This means that $x > 4$ or $x < -4$.

There are many famous inequalities which occur in higher mathematics. I close this chapter with just one of these. You doubtless have dealt with the *arithmetic mean* (AM) or average of n *positive* numbers:

$$\text{AM} = \frac{a_1 + a_2 + \cdots + a_n}{n}.$$

Perhaps you also recognize the *geometric mean* (GM):

$$\text{GM} = \sqrt[n]{a_1 \times a_2 \times \cdots \times a_n}$$

The remarkable inequality to which I refer is that

$$\text{GM} \leq \text{AM}$$

in all cases. I shall prove this for $n = 2$. In this case

$$\text{GM} = \sqrt{a_1 a_2}, \qquad \text{AM} = \frac{a_1 + a_2}{2}.$$

From simple algebra it follows that

$$a_1 a_2 = \frac{(a_1 + a_2)^2}{4} - \frac{(a_1 - a_2)^2}{4}.$$

Since $(a_1 - a_2)^2 \geq 0$, we see that

$$a_1 a_2 \leq \frac{(a_1 + a_2)^2}{4}$$

or that

$$\sqrt{a_1 a_2} \leq \frac{a_1 + a_2}{2}.$$

If you do not believe this, try a few examples. For $a_1 = 2$,

$a_2 = 8$, we have

$$\sqrt{2 \times 8} \leq \frac{2 + 8}{2} \qquad \text{or} \qquad 4 \leq 5.$$

For $a_1 = 5$, $a_2 = 5$, we have

$$\sqrt{5 \times 5} \leq \frac{5 + 5}{2} \qquad \text{or} \qquad 5 \leq 5.$$

It never fails!

Further we can ask: When does equality hold in the statement GM $\leq$ AM? In our proof above for $n = 2$, it is clear that we obtain inequality if $(a_1 - a_2)^2 > 0$ and equality if $(a_1 - a_2)^2 = 0$. Hence equality holds if and only if $a_1 = a_2$. The conclusion is still valid for the general case, that is, equality holds if and only if $a_1, a_2 \ldots , a_n$ are all equal.

PROBLEMS

1. Fill in the correct inequality symbols ($>$ or $<$):

(a) $5 \underline{\hspace{1cm}} (-3)$

(b) $(-10) \underline{\hspace{1cm}} (-7)$

(c) $(-3) \underline{\hspace{1cm}} 8$

(d) $7 \underline{\hspace{1cm}} (-15)$

(e) $(-12) \underline{\hspace{1cm}} 0$

(f) $13 \underline{\hspace{1cm}} 0$

(g) $(-13) \underline{\hspace{1cm}} (-7)$

(h) $48 - 10 \underline{\hspace{1cm}} 10 - 48$

2. Fill in the correct inequality symbols ($>$ or $<$):

(a) Since $8 > 5$, then $2 \times 8 \underline{\hspace{1cm}} 2 \times 5$.

(b) Since $2 < 7$, then $3 \times 2 \underline{\hspace{1cm}} 3 \times 7$.

(c) $4 \times 6 \underline{\hspace{1cm}} 4 \times 10$.

(d) $4 \times (-8) \underline{\hspace{1cm}} 4 \times (-16)$.

(e) Since $6 > 2$, then $(-3) \times 6 \underline{\hspace{1cm}} (-3) \times 2$.

(f) Since $-3 < 5$, then $(-4) \times (-3) \underline{\hspace{1cm}} (-4) \times 5$.

(g) $2 \times 12 \underline{\hspace{1cm}} 2 \times 3$.

(h) $(-3) \times 5 \underline{\hspace{1cm}} (-3) \times 7$.

(i) $4 \times (-8) \underline{\hspace{1cm}} 4 \times (-5)$.

(j) $(-5) \times (-9) \underline{\hspace{1cm}} (-5) \times 0$.

3. Fill in the correct inequality symbols ($>$ or $<$):

(a) Since $(-6) < 10$, then $-6 + 3 \underline{\hspace{1cm}} 10 + 3$.

(b) Since $(-11) < (-5)$, then $-11 + 15 \underline{\hspace{1cm}} -5 + 15$.

(c) $17 - 6 \underline{\hspace{1cm}} 2 - 6$.

(d) $(-2) + 3 \underline{\hspace{1cm}} 4 + 3$.

(e) Since $12 > 5$ and $5 > 1$, then $12 \underline{\hspace{1cm}} 1$.

(f) Since $3 < 6$ and $6 < 10$, then $3 \underline{\hspace{1cm}} 10$.

  (g) Since $7 > 3$, then $\frac{1}{7}$ _____ $\frac{1}{3}$.
  (h) Since $2 < 11$, then $\frac{1}{2}$ _____ $\frac{1}{11}$.
  (i) Since $16 > 9$, then 4 _____ 3.
  (j) Since $(-4)^2 > (-3)^2$, then (-4) _____ (-3).

4. Simplify and plot the graph of the solution set:
  (a) $8x > 16$.   (f) $2x + 4 \leq 5$.
  (b) $-3x < 6$.   (g) $3x - 1 \geq 5$.
  (c) $4x > 2$.   (h) $5x - 2 \leq 3x + 10$.
  (d) $-5x > 15$.   (i) $-7x + 4 \geq 2x - 5$.
  (e) $x + 2 > 6$.   (j) $3x - 2 \leq 4x - 5$.

5. Write in the form $a < x < b$ or $a \leq x \leq b$ and plot the graph of the
   solution set.
  (a) $|x| < 2$.   (f) $|2x - 5| \leq 8$.
  (b) $|x| < 5$.   (g) $|3x + 6| \leq 9$.
  (c) $|x - 1| < 3$.   (h) $|-x + 2| \leq 7$.
  (d) $|x + 2| < 4$.   (i) $|-2x - 1| \leq 3$.
  (e) $|2x| < 6$.

6. Write in the form: $x > a$ or $x < b$, and plot the solution set.
  (a) $|x| > 3$.   (d) $|2x + 1| > 5$.
  (b) $|x| > 5$.   (e) $|-3x + 6| > 9$.
  (c) $|2x| > 4$.

7. Express as an inequality involving absolute values:
  (a) The distance of x from 4 is less than 6.
  (b) The distance of x from 2 is greater than 5.
  (c) The distance of x from 2 is five times its distance from 6.
  (d) x is farther from 3 than it is from -4.
  (e) The sum of the distances of x from 1 and from 3 is greater than 10.

8. Plot the solution sets of:
  (a) $(x + 2)(x - 4) > 0$.
  (b) $x^2 - 7x + 12 < 0$.
  (c) $x^2 + 4x - 5 \geq 0$.
  (d) $x^2 + x + 2 > 0$.
  (e) $(x - 1)(x + 2)(x - 3) > 0$.

9. Verify that $\text{GM} \leq \text{AM}$ when:
  (a) $a_1 = 3$, $a_2 = 27$.
  (b) $a_1 = 2$, $a_2 = 5$, $a_3 = 100$.
  (c) $a_1 = 4$, $a_2 = 4$, $a_3 = 4$.
  (d) $a_1 = 0$, $a_2 = 5$, $a_3 = 2$.

10. Prove: If $a > b$, and if a and b are positive, then $a^2 > b^2$.

11. Show that, among all rectangles with a fixed perimeter, it is the square
   which has maximum area.

ANSWERS

1. (a) >.   (e) <.
   (b) <.   (f) >.
   (c) <.   (g) <.
   (d) >.   (h) >.

2. (a) >.   (f) >.
   (b) <.   (g) >.
   (c) <.   (h) >.
   (d) >.   (i) <.
   (e) <.   (j) >.

3. (a) <.   (f) <.
   (b) <.   (g) <.
   (c) >.   (h) >.
   (d) <.   (i) >.
   (e) >.   (j) <.

4. (a) $x > 2$.   (f) $x \leq \frac{1}{2}$.

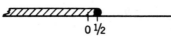

   (b) $x > -2$.   (g) $x \geq 2$.

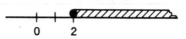

   (c) $x > \frac{1}{2}$.   (h) $x \leq 6$.

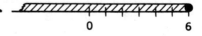

   (d) $x < -3$.   (i) $x \leq 1$.

   (e) $x > 4$.   (j) $x \geq 3$.

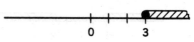

5. (a) $-2 < x < 2$.

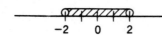

(f) $-3\!\!\:{\scriptstyle\frac{1}{2}} \leq x \leq 13\!\!\:{\scriptstyle\frac{1}{2}}$.

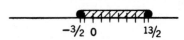

(b) $-5 < x < 5$.

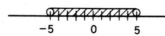

(g) $-5 \leq x \leq 1$.

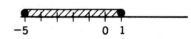

(c) $-3 < x - 1 < 3$ or, better, $-2 < x < 4$.

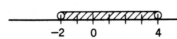

(h) $-5 \leq x \leq 9$.

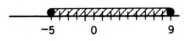

(i) $-2 \leq x \leq 1$.

(d) $-6 < x < 2$.

(e) $-3 < x < 3$.

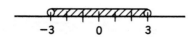

6. (a) $x > 3$ or $x < -3$.   (d) $x > 2$ or $x < -3$.

(b) $x > 5$ or $x < -5$.   (e) $x > 5$ or $x < -1$.

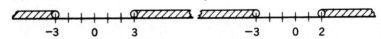

(c) $x > 2$ or $x < -2$.

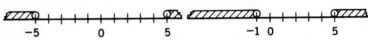

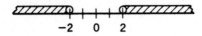

7. (a) $|x - 4| < 6$.
   (b) $|x - 2| > 5$.
   (c) $|x - 2| = 5|x - 6|$.

   (d) $|x - 3| > |x + 4|$.
   (e) $|x - 1| + |x - 3| > 10$.

8. (a)

   (d) The empty set.

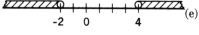

                                                    (e)
   -2   0   4

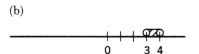

                                    -2   0 1   3
   (b)

       0   3 4

   (c)

   -5   0 1

9. (a) $\sqrt{3 \times 27} < \dfrac{3 + 27}{2}$ or $9 < 15$.

   (b) $\sqrt[3]{2 \times 5 \times 100} < \dfrac{2 + 5 + 100}{3}$ or $10 < 35\frac{2}{3}$.

   (c) $\sqrt[3]{4 \times 4 \times 4} = \dfrac{4 + 4 + 4}{3}$ or $4 = 4$.

   (d) $\sqrt[3]{0 \times 5 \times 2} < \dfrac{0 + 5 + 2}{3}$ or $0 < \frac{7}{3}$.

10. Given: $a - b$ is positive; a is positive; b is positive. Consider: $a^2 - b^2 = (a + b)(a - b)$. By hypothesis each factor on the right is positive. Therefore, the product is positive. Hence $a^2 > b^2$.

11. Let x and y be the length and width, respectively, of a rectangle. Then the area A is xy and the perimeter p is $2x + 2y$. From the fact that $GM \leq AM$ we conclude that

$$\sqrt{xy} \leq \frac{x + y}{2}$$

or that

$$A = xy \leq \left(\frac{x + y}{2}\right)^2 = \left(\frac{p}{4}\right)^2.$$

Therefore, the area is a maximum when equality holds in the above statement, that is, when $x = y$, so that the rectangle is a square.

CHAPTER 10 INEQUALITIES IN THE PLANE

Important applications of inequalities arise from the consideration of inequalities for functions of two or more variables. For the sake of simplicity we shall restrict ourselves here to linear functions of two variables.

Graphs of Linear Inequalities

You are already familiar with functions of this type, for we have seen in Chapter 6 that equations like $3x - 4y + 12 = 0$ represent lines in the X-Y plane. The expression $f(x, y) = 3x - 4y + 12$ is an example of linear function of two variables. Let me recall how we plot the graph of $3x - 4y + 12 = 0$. First we draw the X and Y axes as in Fig. 15. With reference to these we plot the position of points with coordinates (x, y). For example, the point $(3, 1)$ is three units along the X-axis and one unit up the Y-axis. The graph of $3x - 4y + 12 = 0$ consists of those points whose coordinates (x, y) satisfy this equation, and is a straight line. We can plot it by first calculating two of its points. In our example, $(-4, 0)$ and $(0, 3)$ satisfy the equation, so we draw the line as in Fig. 16.

This gives us the points where $3x - 4y + 12 = 0$, but where are those where $3x - 4y + 12 > 0$ or where $3x - 4y + 12 < 0$? Let us examine a few points below the line. At O $(0, 0)$, $3x - 4y + 12 = 12 > 0$. At $(2, 1)$, $3x - 4y + 12 = 6 - 4 + 12 = 14 > 0$, and, at $(4, 4)$, $3x - 4y + 12 = 12 - 16 + 12 = 8 > 0$. Indeed, it is true that, at any point below the line, $3x - 4y + 12 > 0$. Similar

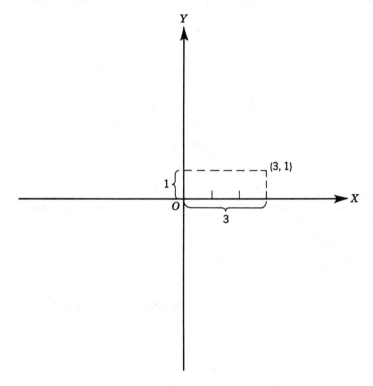

Fig. 15. Coordinate axes.

calculations show that for points above the line $3x - 4y + 12 < 0$. You must not jump at generalizations here, for the situation may be reversed for other functions of this type. For example, $-2x + 3y - 6 > 0$ for points above the line and $-2x + 3y - 6 < 0$ for points below the line (see Fig. 17).

We can, however, make the following true statement: If we draw the line which is the graph of $ax + by + c = 0$, this line divides the plane into two half-planes. In one of these $ax + by + c > 0$, and in the other $ax + by + c < 0$. We can tell which half-plane is which by testing the inequality for a single point not on the line.

PROBLEM.   Sketch the half-plane in which $2x + 5y - 10 > 0$. (See Fig. 18.) First we find that $(0, 2)$ and $(5, 0)$ are on the line, and plot

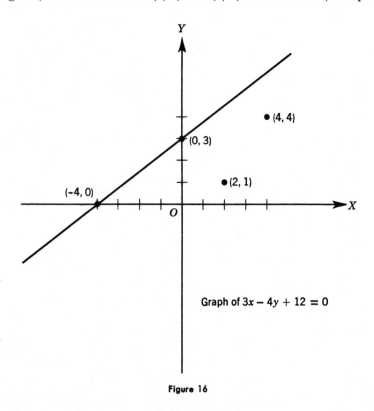

Graph of $3x - 4y + 12 = 0$

Figure 16

them. Join them with the line. Now test any point not on the line; we choose O because the arithmetic is easiest for this point. At O, $2x + 5y - 10 = 0 + 0 - 10 < 0$. Hence the half-plane below the line is the wrong one for our problem, and so the upper half-plane gives us the solution. Just to be sure we check that at $(3, 3)$, $2x + 5y - 10 = 6 + 15 - 10 = 11 > 0$. We now shade the upper half-plane.

We can complicate the problem by seeking the set of pairs (x, y) which are solutions of *both* the inequalities:

$$2x + 5y - 10 > 0 \qquad \text{and} \qquad x - y < 1.$$

We already have discussed the first of these, so let us turn to the second. The line $x - y = 1$ passes through the points $(1, 0)$ and

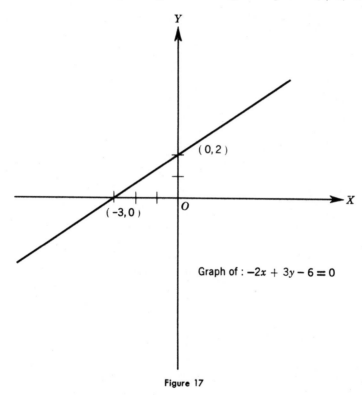

Graph of : $-2x + 3y - 6 = 0$

Figure 17

$(0, -1)$. At O, $x - y = 0 - 0 = 0 < 1$, so the correct half-plane is that which includes the origin. We now plot both lines on the same axes and shade the region which belongs to both selected half-planes. (See Fig. 19.) We can continue this process for as many lines as we please.

This technique of solving systems of inequalities is the first step toward solving many problems of business and industry, and is related to a subject known as *Linear Programing*.

The Basketball Problem

Let us illustrate by considering an imaginary situation in a basketball game. The home team is behind by 3 points and there are $10\frac{1}{2}$ minutes left to play. The home team can put on either a slow-

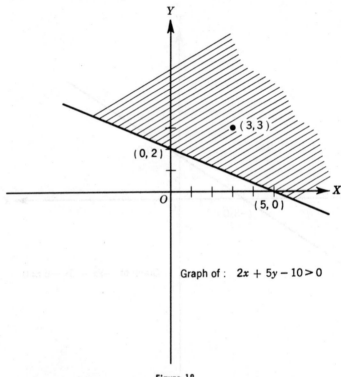

Graph of : $2x + 5y - 10 > 0$

Figure 18

moving pattern offense or a fast, hard-running offense. On the average the following figures are assumed to be accurate:

Offense	Time/Play	Shooting Accuracy
FOR THE HOME TEAM		
Pattern	30 seconds	2 out of 3
Running	15 seconds	1 out of 3
FOR THE OPPONENTS, WHO ALWAYS RUN		
Running	15 seconds	1 out of 2

The home team naturally wishes to win, but also thinks it wise to mix up its offenses as much as possible. What possibilities are open to them?

Let p be the number of pattern plays the home team uses and r the number of running plays, so that the home team has a total of $p + r$ plays. Assume that after each shot the ball changes hands, so

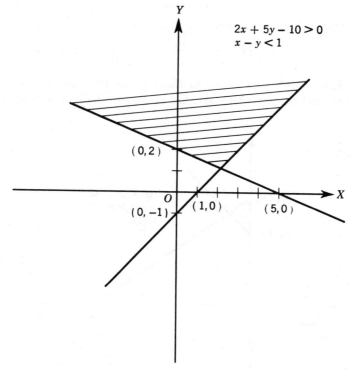

$$2x + 5y - 10 > 0$$
$$x - y < 1$$

$(0, 2)$

$(0, -1)$

$(1, 0)$

$(5, 0)$

Figure 19

that the opponents will also have $p + r$ plays. We must assume, also, that there are no penalties, and no miscues which cause the ball to change hands except after a shot.

Then we look at the time required. We see that

$$30p + 15r + 15(p + r) < (10\tfrac{1}{2})(60) = 630 \quad \text{(seconds)}$$

Dividing by 15 we simplify this to

$$2p + r + (p + r) < 42$$

or

$$3p + 2r < 42.$$

With regard to the score, if the home team is to win we must have

$$2 \times [\tfrac{2}{3}p + \tfrac{1}{3}r - \tfrac{1}{2}(p + r)] > 3.$$

This simplifies to

$$p - r > 9.$$

Our system of inequalities is therefore:

$$3p + 2r < 42, \qquad p \geq 0,$$
$$p - r > 9, \qquad r \geq 0.$$

Their graph is as shown in Fig. 20. The two lines intersect at (3, 12), and the set which satisfies all the inequalities is shaded in

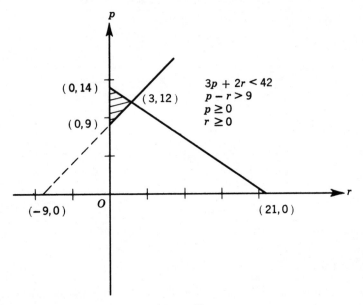

Figure 20

the figure. The home team can then play any combination (r, p) of offenses which lies in the shaded region. The possibilities are:

r	0	1	2
p	9 to 14	11 to 13	12

   In other words, the home team can afford to use at most two running plays. Perhaps they would do better to use the pattern offense for the whole time, but the team will have to decide this on the basis of other information than that stated in this problem.

   For a true problem in Linear Programing we should put the question somewhat differently. Suppose we had said: Given $10\frac{1}{2}$ minutes to play and the times and accuracies stated above, how

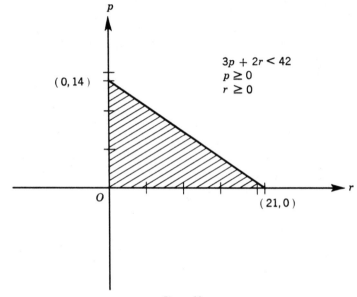

Figure 21

should the running and pattern plays be distributed so that the home team would have the *largest net gain* in score?

   The mathematical formulation then becomes: For what values of p and r is the function (the net gain in score) $p - r$ a maximum when p and r are subject to the conditions

$$3p + 2r < 42, \qquad p \geq 0, \quad r \geq 0.$$

The graph of these simultaneous inequalities is shown in Fig. 21. A theorem says that this maximum will be achieved at one of the vertices of this triangle. Let us check them.

At $(21, 0)$,

$$p - r = 0 - 21 = -21.$$

At (0, 0),
$$p - r = 0.$$
At (0, 14),
$$p - r = 14.$$

The conclusion is that, for the largest net score, all plays should be pattern plays. This conclusion was probably obvious to you without all these calculations, but that is inevitable if I give you such a simple problem. The point is that methods of this kind can solve maximization problems of much greater difficulty for which the solutions are far from obvious. Let me illustrate the method by a second example.

The Diet Problem

This illustration is a simplified version of one of the original problems that led to the invention of Linear Programing. Let us suppose that we have two types of synthetic foods, which I call A and B. You may think of K rations and C rations if you like, but the numbers given below are purely artificial and apply to no foods on the market. Let us suppose that the two foods contain the following nutritional components:

Food	Calories per Ounce	Protein per Ounce	Fat per Ounce
A	100	50	0
B	200	10	30

The units for protein and fat are arbitrary and need not be specified.

Let us also suppose that the minimum daily requirements for an active man are:

Calories: 2500.
Protein: 350.
Fat: 150.

There are several different questions that can now be asked. As a starter consider our first problem:

PROBLEM 1. Which food or combination of foods should be employed in order: (a) to fulfill the minimum daily nutritional requirements, and (b) to minimize the total weight?

Such a problem would be of importance to a mountain climber, or to a military expedition. In order to attack the problem I must introduce some notation.

Let a represent the number of ounces of food A that are required,
b represent the number of ounces of food B that are required.
Then the minimum daily requirements will be met if:

Calories: $100a + 200b \geq 2500.$
Protein: $50a + 10b \geq 350.$
Fat: $30b \geq 150.$

These three inequalities can be simplified to the following simultaneous system:

$$a + 2b \geq 25,$$
$$5a + b \geq 35,$$
$$b \geq 5.$$

To these we should also add the practical requirements that $a \geq 0$ and $b \geq 0$, for one cannot eat a negative amount of food. The graph of these inequalities is given in Fig. 22. In this figure the shaded region represents the possible pairs (a, b) which meet the minimum daily requirements.

Now I must turn to the quantity which is to be minimized, namely, the total weight, $W = a + b$. The basic theorem on Linear Programing says that W will be a minimum at one of the *vertices* labeled P, Q, R in the figure. In order to determine which vertex to use, let us do some arithmetic.

At P,

$$a = 0, \qquad b = 35, \qquad W = a + b = 35.$$

At Q,

$$a = 5, \qquad b = 10, \qquad W = a + b = 15.$$

At R,

$$a = 15, \qquad b = 5, \qquad W = a + b = 20.$$

Therefore, W is a minimum at Q, and the diet should consist of 5 ounces of food A and 10 ounces of food B.

For variety we can change the problem to consider feeding the consumer for the least cost, as in Problem 2.

PROBLEM 2. Let us assume all the above information plus the fact that food A costs 10 cents per ounce and food B costs 20 cents per ounce. Then what combination of A and B should be used to provide an adequate diet at least cost?

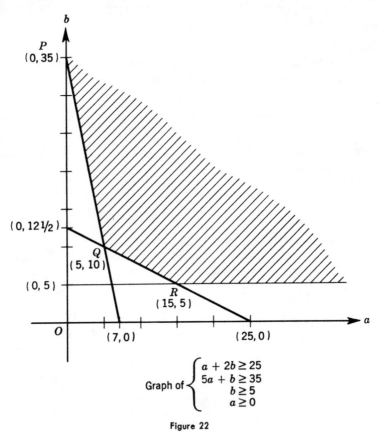

Graph of $\begin{cases} a + 2b \ge 25 \\ 5a + b \ge 35 \\ b \ge 5 \\ a \ge 0 \end{cases}$

Figure 22

The solution is just as given above until we come to select one of the points P, Q, or R. Now we consider the following:

$$\text{Cost} = 10a + 20b.$$

At P,

$$a = 0, \qquad b = 35, \qquad \text{cost} = 700 \text{ cents.}$$

At Q,

$$a = 5, \qquad b = 10, \qquad \text{cost} = 250 \text{ cents.}$$

At R,
$$a = 15, \qquad b = 5, \qquad \text{cost} = 250 \text{ cents.}$$

Thus Q and R are equally good solutions, and in fact any point on the segment QR is also a solution.

PROBLEMS

1. Plot the graphs of the solution sets of the inequalities:
   (a) $x + 3y + 6 > 0$.
   (b) $2x - y + 4 > 0$.
   (c) $(x + y + 1)^2 \geq 0$.
2. Plot the graph of the solution set of the simultaneous inequalities:
$$2x - y - 1 > 0,$$
$$3x + 4y - 7 > 0.$$
3. In the diet problem suppose that the consumers *dislike* food A six times as intensely as they dislike food B. Then what combination of A and B should be used to minimize the amount of griping?
4. In the diet problem suppose that 1 ounce of food A occupies 2 cubic inches and that 1 ounce of food B occupies 3 cubic inches. Then what combination of A and B should be used to minimize the total volume? Such a decision might be important to an astronaut.
5. The situation in a simplified version of a football game is as follows. There are just two plays, a running play and a pass play. We assume these facts to be true:

Play	Distance Gained, yards	Time Required, seconds
Running	3	30
Pass	12	9

Also suppose that there are 36 yards to go for a touchdown and that 138 seconds remain in the game. Ignore the requirement of having to make 10 yards in four downs and other considerations of score and strategy. *Problem:* What combinations of running and pass plays will secure a touchdown in the allotted time?
6. In the football problem (Prob. 5 above) suppose that on the average there is one injury in each five running plays and one injury in each ten pass plays. Then what combination of plays should the quarterback call to secure the touchdown in the allotted time with the minimum risk of injuries?

7. The Minneapolis and Seattle Lumber Company can convert logs into either lumber or pulp. In a given week the mill can turn out 500 units of production, of which 100 units of lumber and 200 units of pulp are required by regular customers. The profit on a unit of lumber is $15 and on a unit of pulp is $18. *Problem:* How many units of lumber and pulp should the mill produce (totaling 500) in order to maximize the total profit?

ANSWERS

1. (a)   (b)

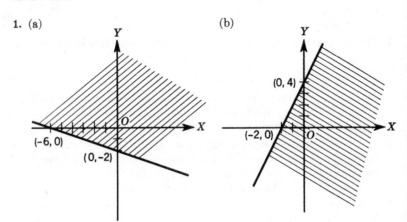

(c) The entire plane.

2.

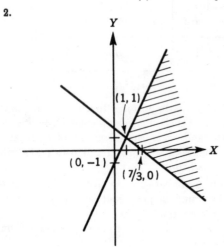

3. Let D be the measure of dislike.
   At P, $a = 0$, $b = 35$, $D = 6a + b = 35$.
   At Q, $a = 5$, $b = 10$, $D = 30 + 10 = 40$.
   At R, $a = 15$, $b = 5$, $D = 90 + 5 = 95$.
   Answer: Use P where $a = 0$, $b = 35$.

4. Let V = volume.
   At P, $a = 0$, $b = 35$, $V = 2a + 3b = 105$ cubic inches.
   At Q, $a = 5$, $b = 10$, $V = 40$ cubic inches.
   At R, $a = 15$, $b = 5$, $V = 45$ cubic inches.
   Answer: Use Q where $a = 5$, $b = 10$.

5. The inequalities are: Distance: $3r + 12p \geq 36$. Time: $30r + 9p \leq 138$.
   Also $p \geq 0$, $r \geq 0$. These simplify to

$$r + 4p \geq 12,$$
$$10r + 3p \leq 46,$$
$$p \geq 0,$$
$$r \geq 0.$$

The graph is shown below. The shaded triangle is the solution set. The

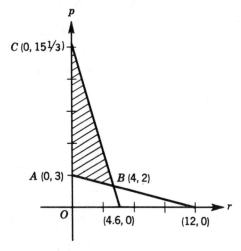

pairs of integers corresponding to pairs in this triangle are:

r	0	1	2	3	4
p	3 to 15	3 to 12	3 to 8	3 to 5	2

From among these possibilities the quarterback can choose his plays
according to his judgment of appropriate strategy.

6. Let I = injuries. Then $I = \dfrac{r}{5} + \dfrac{p}{10}$.

At A, $r = 0$, $p = 3$; $I = \frac{3}{10}$.
At B, $r = 4$, $p = 2$; $I = \frac{4}{5} + \frac{2}{10} = 1$.
At C, $r = 0$, $p = 15\frac{1}{3}$; $I = \frac{46}{30} = 1.53$.
I is minimized at A, so the quarterback calls three pass plays and no running plays.

7. Let L = units of lumber, P = units of pulp.
The conditions are:

$$L + P = 500, \qquad L \geq 100, \quad P \geq 200.$$

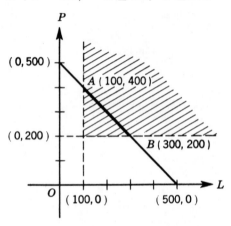

Profit $= 15L + 18P$. Draw the graph. From the two inequalities the mill must operate in the shaded portion of the plane. Moreover, it must operate along the diagonal line. Hence its operations must lie on the segment AB.

At A, $L = 100$, $P = 400$; profit $= 15L + 18P = 8700$.
At B, $L = 300$, $P = 200$; profit $= 15L + 18P = 8100$.

Hence the mill should operate at A and produce 100 units of lumber and 400 units of pulp.

CHAPTER 11 GEOMETRY

The traditional program in geometry included Euclidean plane geometry in the tenth grade and solid geometry in the twelfth grade. There was some attempt to introduce simple geometrical ideas in the elementary school, and formulas for areas and volume were often given in the eighth grade. In general, however, geometry was put off till the tenth grade, and very few pupils reached solid geometry at all.

For centuries geometry has been considered to be one of the most important subjects in the education of an intelligent man, and the course goes back with remarkably little change to the days of Euclid in 300 B.C. It is no exaggeration to say that every educated man in the world who lived after the time of Euclid studied geometry much as it is taught today. What is it about geometry that has caused it to last so long and to be so popular with men of all ages and of all countries? Of course, it has immense practical value, for one must know something about geometry to deal with the shapes of physical objects, and the craftsman, the mechanic, and the artisan must be highly skilled in geometry to ply their trades. I believe, however, that the real reason is deeper. Euclid's great accomplishment was to construct the first formal mathematical model of nature. He presented the first systematic treatment of axioms and initiated the procedure of deducing conclusions from premises. Geometry is thus the prototype of a major trend in civilized thought, and every civilized man needs to know it if he is to understand other aspects of his surroundings. Geometry has been, therefore, a liberal art in the true sense, and not merely a tool for science and technology. There are those who have tried to reduce it to such a tool, but they have missed the sweep of history as it applies to geometry.

When the revolution in mathematics approached the subject of geometry, there was much less agreement than in other areas of school mathematics. There are those who argue for drastic curtailment of instruction in geometry on the grounds (1) that its place as a prime example of the axiomatic method has been usurped by algebra in its modern axiomatic form, and (2) that the time spent on geometry could be more profitably devoted to more algebra and even calculus. Others favor an overhauling of Euclid's geometry to take account of modern scholarship, and still others argue for the replacement of much Euclidean geometry by analytic geometry. The issue is far from settled, and so almost anything is likely to be happening in your school. Let me describe for you some of the ideas that are in the air.

What's Wrong with Euclid?

The first topic concerns the modern revision of Euclid's *Elements*. Euclid claimed to have provided a set of axioms from which all of the theorems of geometry could be proved by logical means. His work was so skillful that no one found a flaw until about one hundred years ago, some 2200 years after Euclid. There are very few men whose work has stood up so well! But a serious flaw was found, and it is now proposed that this be remedied in our school teaching of geometry.

Euclid warned us to reason from the axioms and not to argue from a figure, but in one important place he failed to follow his own warning. Apparently he never noticed that it is necessary to be careful about the *order* of points on a line. Let us illustrate the problem by attempting to define a *line segment*. If we are given two points,

A and *B*, on a line (see Fig. 23), we wish to speak of the *segment AB*. The natural definition of this segment is that it consists of the points *A* and *B* and all points on the line *between* them. The trouble is that Euclid's axioms give us no grounds for deciding what *between* should mean. Of course, we know what we mean from the figure, but this is not enough—it must be in the axioms. By straightening out

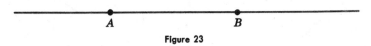

Figure 23

this notion of *betweenness*, mathematicians of the last century cleared up many obscurities in Euclid. It is strange that writers of school textbooks have ignored this development for some seventy-five years!

There is a similar problem in Euclid regarding points in a plane. We surely know what we mean by a triangle, but what does it mean

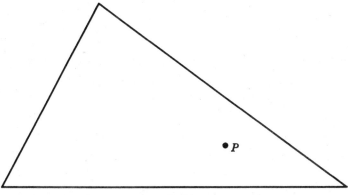

Figure 24

to say that a point *P* is *inside* a triangle? In Fig. 24 this is clear, but how else does one describe this fact? Of the several alternative approaches, perhaps the simplest is to add the following axiom:

Axiom. Every line divides the plane into three subsets which have no point in common:

    (1) The line itself.
    (2) The set I (intuitively the points on one side of the line).

(3) The set II (the points on the other side of the line) such that (See Fig. 25a and b):

(a) A segment PQ lies in I (or II) if and only if the points P and Q are in region I (or II).

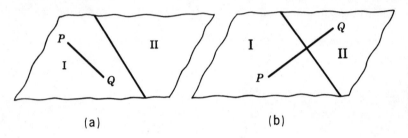

(a)   (b)

Fig. 25. Division of a plane by a line.

(b) A segment PQ intersects the given line if and only if its end points P and Q are in opposite regions, I and II, or II and I.

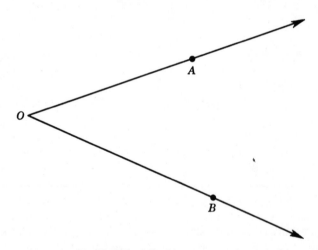

Fig. 26. Angle defined by two rays.

This may seem trivial to you, and it certainly is obvious. But rigorous geometry cannot be done without this axiom or one equivalent to it. Let me show you how this is applied in textbooks now written for seventh-grade students.

An angle is defined to be a pair of *rays* (or half-lines) each start-ing at a point O and extending indefinitely in one direction. (See Fig. 26.) We pick points A and B respectively on the rays, and speak of the angle AOB. Now we must define the *interior* of this angle. (See Fig. 27.) The line of which OA is a part divides the plane into two half-planes. In one of these we find the point B. Let us call this the B-side of OA. Similarly, we can speak of the A-side of OB. Finally, we define the interior of angle AOB to be the set of points which are in both the B-side of OA and the A-side of OB. We have

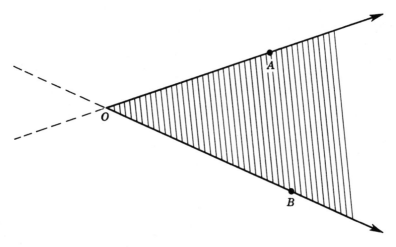

Fig. 27. Interior of angle AOB.

previously called this the *intersection* of those two half-planes. The shaded region pictures this set. From this we can proceed to define the *interior* of the triangle ABC. This is the intersection of the interiors of the three vertex angles of the triangle.

But, you ask, why do we need to define this, for was it not obvious before? Yes it was, but we had no way of proving anything about this interior. If you re-examine your old geometry book, you will find many proofs that tacitly suppose that certain points are inside a given triangle but which never prove that this is the case. Using the above method we can now construct such a proof. I agree that this makes many proofs long and tedious and do not recommend such proofs in every case. We should, however, understand what is involved and be able to fill in the details if necessary.

Analytic Geometry

The methods of Euclidean geometry are far from automatic. They often require that certain lines be constructed (for no obvious reason) and that great ingenuity be used. By transferring our problems to analytic geometry we can work with numbers and algebra and hence get solutions with less mental effort. Since analytic geometry is used widely in calculus and in the applications of mathematics to physics and engineering, it is recommended that it be introduced at an early stage in the high school curriculum. Clearly this introduction would leave less time for the standard deductive geometry, and so there is a conflict of interests. How do we weigh the cultural and imaginative aspects of deductive geometry against the power and applicability of analytic geometry? This is an old battle and it is not likely to be settled easily.

Intuitive Geometry

In Chapter 1 I described how important it is to begin any mathematical subject with intuition before proceeding to its formal, systematic treatment. This precept applies with special force to geometry. It is madness to begin geometry in the tenth grade in an axiomatic, deductive fashion unless a foundation of intuition is built first. If we have to build this foundation in the tenth grade, there is hardly time left to do a proper job with the deductive material. Moreover, the tenth grade is too late for students to begin their geometrical studies; they need the information earlier.

In view of this situation the modern textbooks introduce geometry in the seventh grade or earlier. The emphasis here is on the *ideas* rather than on the proofs. Applications are made to daily affairs such as explaining why a three-legged stool sits firmly on the floor, whereas a four-legged chair may wobble. This early teaching of geometry is an excellent scheme, which has the approval of everyone involved.

Solid Geometry

It is a paradox that in the space age the teaching of the geometry of space has gone to pieces. But so it is, and the fault is due to both neglect and misunderstanding. Everyone agreed that the old twelfth-grade course in solid geometry had failed to meet its objectives, but there was no agreement on the remedy. Students have a serious need for an understanding of space relationships, for knowledge of the facts about lines and planes in space, and for information about the geometry of the sphere (for is our globe not a sphere?). The deductive method of approaching these ideas was too complicated and tiresome, and seemed to bog down in details while missing the main ideas. For this reason it was recommended that the course be abandoned, and that the material on space geometry be taught intuitively in the junior high school and in the tenth grade. This has been partially accomplished, but much more must be done. Too often space geometry is taught nowhere in the school, and our children are the worse for our neglect.

A Recommendation

My own preference for the geometry curriculum is the following:

Junior High. Intuitive geometry in two and three dimensions. Emphasize ideas; no proof.

Tenth Grade. Modernized deductive geometry of the plane. Ideas of solid geometry introduced where appropriate. A few weeks only of analytic geometry.

Twelfth Grade. One semester of plane and solid analytic geometry. A few weeks on the geometry of the sphere.

If this program is followed in addition to a proper curriculum in algebra and trigonometry, the student will be well prepared for his calculus course when he goes to college. It is very foolish to teach calculus to anyone who has not first completed such a curriculum.

A Theorem on Intersections

Let us now get down to some details. First I shall show you an application of the axiom on the division of the plane which I stated earlier in the chapter.

Theorem 1. *Given: A triangle ABC and a line PQ (see Fig. 28) which intersects segment BC but which does not pass through any of the vertices A, B, C.*
Conclusion: Line *PQ* intersects either segment *AB* or segment *AC*.

Proof:
1. Let us suppose that line *PQ* does not intersect segment *AB*. Then we must prove that it does intersect segment *AC*.
2. Line *PQ* intersects segment *BC* (hypothesis).
3. *B* and *C* are on opposite sides of line *PQ* (axiom above).

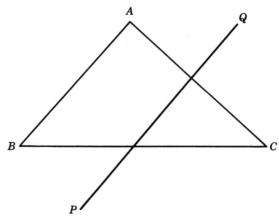

Figure 28

4. Line *PQ* does not intersect segment *AB* (assumed).
5. *A* and *B* lie on the same side of line *PQ* (axiom above).
6. *A* and *C* are on opposite sides of line *PQ* (steps 3 and 5).
7. Line *PQ* intersects segment *AC* (axiom above).

Inside and Outside

The matter of defining the inside of a triangle was simple enough, but it is harder with other figures. The generalization of the definition of the inside of a triangle, for instance, does not work for a polygon such as that in Fig. 29. Moreover, how can you determine in a simple way whether point *P* in Fig. 30 is inside or outside the polygon of the figure? A good method is to draw a ray *PQ* not through any of the vertices and to count the number of sides which it crosses. Regardless of how you draw *PQ* this number will be *even* if *P* is outside and *odd* if *P* is inside. Try a few positions for *PQ*, and check this for yourself. Of course, this result requires proof, but since the proof is complicated I shall leave it out. The idea, however, is most important. Did you ever run across it when you were in school?

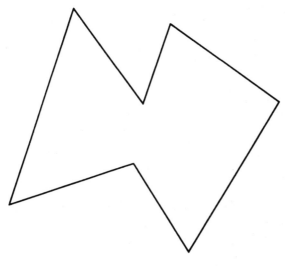

Figure 29

Euler's Theorem

Finally I shall turn to a result in solid geometry which has great intuitive appeal, but which disappeared from school geometries several generations ago.

First consider a triangular pyramid such as that in Fig. 31. This is called a tetrahedron, a word derived from the Greek *tetra*, which means four. Let us count the number of vertices, edges, and faces. We get: V (vertices) $= 4$, E (edges) $= 6$, F (faces) $= 4$. Now compute: $N = V - E + F = 4 - 6 + 4 = 2$. For later use we record this:

Tetrahedron: $N = 2$.

Figure 30

Next do the same for a cube (see Fig. 32). We find that $V = 8$, $E = 12$, $F = 6$, so that $N = V - E + F = 2$.

Cube: $N = 2$.

Finally let us do it for an octahedron (Fig. 33). We find that $V = 6$, $E = 12$, $F = 8$, so that $N = V - E + F = 2$.

Octahedron: $N = 2$.

Perhaps this is getting monotonous; we seem to get $N = 2$ no matter what solid figure we consider. As I shall show you, this is not necessarily the case, so we need to state some property of a solid

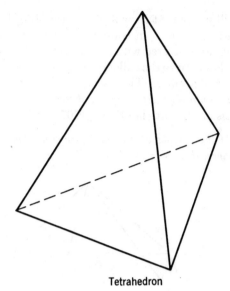

Tetrahedron

Figure 31

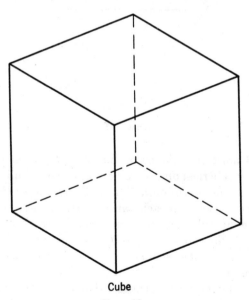

Cube

Figure 32

figure which will imply that $N = 2$. What, then, do the tetrahedron, cube, and octahedron have in common? Let us suppose that they are made of wire and covered with a thin rubber surface like that of a balloon. Now blow air into the balloon—eventually the rubber surface will become that of a sphere. That is, *the surface of each of these solids can be blown up into the surface of a sphere.* The result before us is due to the Swiss mathematician Euler (1707–1782) and is as follows:

Theorem 2.   *If the surface of a solid figure can be blown up into the surface of a sphere, then $N = V - E + F = 2$.*

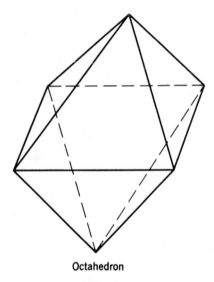

Octahedron

Figure 33

Again, I must omit the proof, but let us try some experiments. First take any spherical object (say an orange or a billiard ball) and draw a network of curves on it. Mark all the intersections and call these "vertices". Between each pair of vertices there should be one and only one curved segment—call this an "edge". Call the open spaces "faces". Now compute $V - E + F$; if you have followed the instructions this number should be $N = 2$. Thus you have verified Euler's Theorem.

As the next experiment I suggest that you do the same thing on the surface of a doughnut. I know that it is hard to draw on a doughnut, so I suggest that you try it on a rubber ring such as is used in deck tennis or quoits. Each "face" must be polygonal—ring-shaped regions do not fit the requirements. If you do this carefully you will find that $N = 0$. Why not $N = 2$? The answer is that there is no way of blowing up the surface of a doughnut into the surface of a sphere. Further experiments of this kind are suggested in the problems.

Regular Solids

Let me return to Euler's Theorem as it applies to solids whose surface can be blown up into the surface of a sphere. Remember that in this case

$$V - E + F = 2.$$

A solid is called *regular* if and only if each face has the same number of edges, and if each vertex is met by the same number of edges. The question now is: What regular solids exist?

Let n represent the number of edges to a face and m represent the number of edges meeting at a vertex. Then the three solids mentioned above are regular with the following values of n and m:

Solid	m (edges per vertex)	n (edges per face)
Tetrahedron	3	3
Cube	3	4
Octahedron	4	3

Since there are F faces, the number of edges can be counted by considering the product nF. This counts each edge twice, so we have the relation

$$nF = 2E \quad \text{or} \quad F = 2E/n.$$

In a similar way we can find that

$$mV = 2E, \quad \text{or} \quad V = 2E/m.$$

Now substitute these expressions for F and V in $V - E + F = 2$. The result is

$$\frac{2E}{m} - E + \frac{2E}{n} = 2,$$

which can be rewritten in the form

$$\frac{1}{m} + \frac{1}{n} = \frac{1}{2} + \frac{1}{E}.$$

The problem now is to find all possible values of n, m, and E (integers!) which satisfy this equation. To do so we construct the table shown.

m	n	E	V	F	Solid
3	3	6	4	4	Tetrahedron
3	4	12	8	6	Cube
3	5	30	20	12	Dodecahedron
3	6	—	—	—	Impossible since $\frac{1}{3} + \frac{1}{6} = \frac{1}{2}$
3	7	—	—	—	Impossible since $\frac{1}{3} + \frac{1}{7} < \frac{1}{2}$
4	3	12	6	8	Octahedron
4	4	—	—	—	Impossible since $\frac{1}{4} + \frac{1}{4} = \frac{1}{2}$
4	5	—	—	—	Impossible since $\frac{1}{4} + \frac{1}{5} < \frac{1}{2}$
5	3	30	12	20	Icosahedron
5	4	—	—	—	Impossible since $\frac{1}{5} + \frac{1}{4} < \frac{1}{2}$

Other choices for m and n are also impossible.

Thus there are exactly five regular solids: tetrahedron, cube, octahedron, dodecahedron, and icosahedron (Fig. 34).

This result was known to the Greeks at least as early as the fourth century B.C., and was used extensively by Plato in the devel-

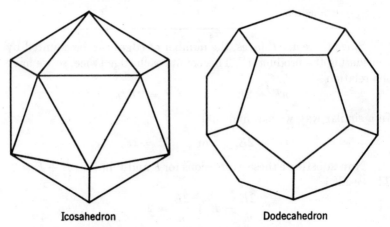

Icosahedron   Dodecahedron

Figure 34

opment of his philosophy. Hence, the five regular solids are often called the "Platonic Solids". It is a beautiful theorem, but of little practical importance. Students of mathematics, however, should see such theorems in order to be convinced that mathematics has aesthetic as well as practical values.

PROBLEMS

1. Find the flaw in the following proof that: *All triangles are isosceles.*

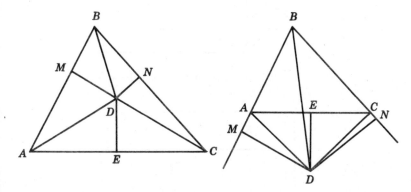

(a) Given triangle ABC, construct the angle bisector BD at angle B and the perpendicular bisector DE of side AC. Unless $AB = BC$, these lines are distinct and meet in a point D. So far as we know at present, D may lie inside or outside the triangle, so we draw the two corresponding figures.

(b) Draw AD and DC.

(c) From D draw $MD \perp AB$ and $ND \perp BC$.

(d) $\triangle ADE \cong \triangle CDE$ (right triangles with equal bases and altitudes).

(e) $AD = DC$ (corresponding parts of congruent triangles).

(f) $\triangle BMD \cong \triangle BND$ (right triangles with equal angles at B and equal sides BD).

(g) $MD = ND$ and $BM = BN$ (corresponding parts of congruent triangles).

(h) $\triangle ADM \cong \triangle CDN$ (right triangles with two pairs of equal sides).

(i) $AM = CN$ (corresponding parts of congruent triangles).

(j) In the first figure above,   In the second figure above,

$$BM = BN,$$
$$AM = CN.$$

$$BM = BN,$$
$$AM = CN.$$

Adding: $AB = BC$.   Subtracting: $AB = BC$.

2. Compute $N = V - E + F$ for the subdivision of the doughnut suggested by the figure.

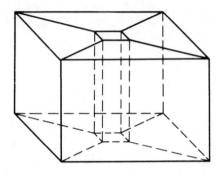

3. Compute $N = V - E + F$ for the doughnut with two holes, as sketched below.

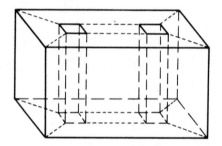

4. On the basis of your previous experiences guess the value of N for a doughnut with q holes. This is an exercise in intuition—now someone must prove your guess to be right or wrong. Probably this is beyond you, but it is fun to try!

5. Compute N for the doughnut using a subdivision different from that in Prob. 2. You should again get $N = 0$.

6. Compute N for the doughnut with two holes using a subdivision different from that in Prob. 3. You should again get $N = -2$.

ANSWERS

1. D must lie outside the triangle, for it lies on the circumscribed circle. Even so, the figures above are incorrect. Either M lies on segment AB or N lies on segment BC, but not both. So on one side we should subtract and on the other side we should add.

This fallacy illustrates the point that we should never argue from a figure. In order to handle this problem we need the concept of the order of points on a line, phrased in a way such that we can prove results without the use of a figure. The modern treatment of geometry permits this; Euclid's does not.

2. $V = 16; E = 32; F = 16; N = V - E + F = 0.$

3. $V = 24; E = 48; F = 32; N = V = E + F = -2.$

4. $N = 2 - 2q.$

CHAPTER 12 TRIGONOMETRY

The word *trigonometry* means the science of measuring a triangle. This science was invented to enable us to calculate the magnitudes of unknown sides and angles of a triangle provided that we were given the magnitudes of enough sides and angles for the triangle to be determined. In this way it is possible for us to measure inaccessible distances such as heights of mountains and widths of rivers by measuring other distances and angles and then using the formulas of trigonometry. The method was also applied to the geometry of triangles on a sphere, and this led to important applications to astronomy and celestial navigation. Since computations of this kind involve lengthy arithmetic, it has been customary to carry them out by means of logarithms, and so instruction in the use of logarithms has commonly found its place in courses on trigonometry.

In developing the relations among the trigonometric functions which were needed for these purposes, mathematicians amassed a considerable theory which is not directly related to the measurement of the triangle. This subject is known as *analytic trigonometry*, and it has many applications in calculus and in other branches of higher mathematics. Thus, trigonometry has been viewed as a subject with both practical and theoretical aspects, both of which were important in the education of a prospective scientist or engineer.

The traditional course in trigonometry defined the trigonometric functions, used them to solve right and oblique triangles by means of logarithms, and then spent the little time that was left on trigonometric identities, graphs, and equations. Sometimes the inverse trigonometric functions were included.

Such a course, no matter how well conceived in the past, is extremely unsuitable as part of a modern school curriculum in mathematics. The original purposes of trigonometry had to do with surveying and celestial navigation, but how many of our children are going along one of these paths? Surveying is a small and essential profession, but its methods are a far cry from those suggested in textbooks on trigonometry. In particular, I have been told by professional surveyers that computation by logarithms has long since been obsolete in the profession—they use desk calculators to work up their data. Similarly, celestial navigation—once the greatest friend of sea captains—has been replaced by modern electronic aids. I agree that I would feel more comfortable on a sea voyage if the skipper knew how to shoot the sun and compute his position, and I hope this art is not lost. Nevertheless, the basic navigation of ships and aircraft is done by other means, and celestial navigation is for the occasional specialist.

If the old applications are as obsolete as this, you may ask why the course has persisted in its present form. The only reason that I can give is that of sheer inertia and conservatism. There is no course in the mathematics curriculum that could stand a greater change.

Definitions of Trigonometric Functions

How, then, is it being modernized in the better schools? The most striking change is that modern trigonometry (in spite of its name) has very little to do with triangles, or even with angles for that matter. The first change that I shall discuss is the definition of the trigonometric functions themselves, so that they are functions not of angles but of real numbers like most other functions. From your school days you will recall that, in the right triangle ABC, we define the sine of angle A to be the *opposite over the hypoteneuse* or

a/c. Similarly, the cosine of A is b/c. (See Fig. 35.) We write these for short:

$$\sin A = a/c,$$
$$\cos A = b/c.$$

In these formulas A is supposed to be an angle measured in degrees or possibly in radians.

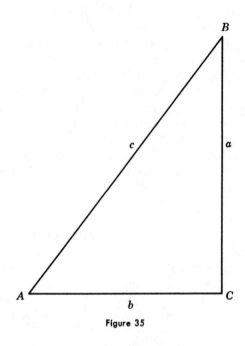

Figure 35

In other mathematical functions the variable does not stand for an angle but a real number. For instance in

$$f(x) = x^2 - 4x + 7,$$

or

$$g(x) = \log_{10} x,$$

we understand that we are to substitute numbers for x. In this way we compute $f(2) = 4 - 8 + 7 = 3$ and $g(2) = 0.3031$. Traditionally, however, it has been nonsense to write sin 2 unless we state whether 2 is measured in degrees or radians.

This is an intolerable state of affairs, for in calculus and in modern applications of trigonometry to electrical engineering we regularly meet sin 2 with no such specification of units for 2. Let me give you the modern definition of sin x and cos x. First we draw a

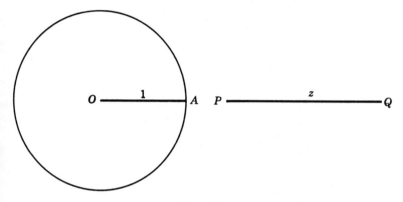

Figure 36

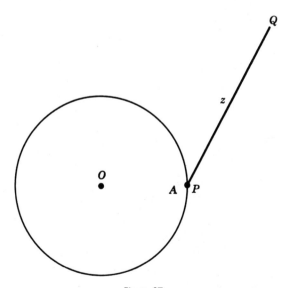

Figure 37

circle of radius one, and to the same scale a segment PQ of length z (Fig. 36). Let us think of PQ as a flexible piece of inextensible wire and place the end P at the point A on the circle (Fig. 37). Now wrap PQ around the circle as far as it will go. The result may look like

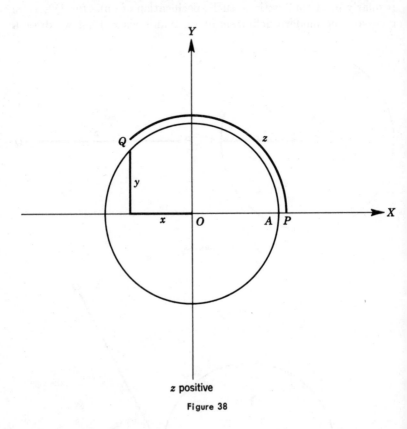

z positive

Figure 38

that in Fig. 38. The point Q will then lie on the circle and has coordinates x and y. We then define

$$\sin z = y,$$
$$\cos z = x,$$

where y and x are the coordinates of the point Q.

The above construction assumes that z is positive. If z is negative we wrap the segment of length $|z|$ around the circle in a clockwise direction and thus find the position of point Q (Fig. 39).

From such a figure we can immediately compute the values of these functions for certain convenient values of z.

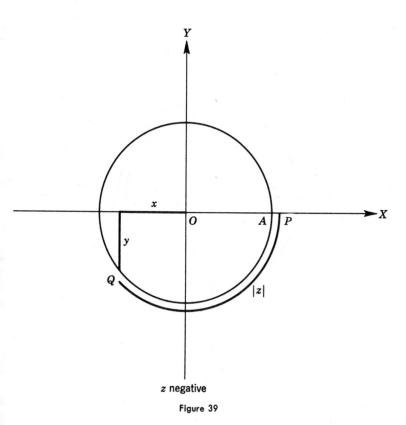

z negative

Figure 39

Since the length of a quarter of a circle is $\pi/2$, we see that $\sin \dfrac{\pi}{2} = 1$, $\cos \dfrac{\pi}{2} = 0$. (See Fig. 40.) Since the length of a semicircle is π, we see that (Fig. 41) $\sin \pi = 0$, $\cos \pi = -1$. The values of $\sin z$ and $\cos z$ for most other values of z cannot be computed so easily, but good decimal approximations can be obtained from a large scale graph. In practice one refers to a table.

With these definitions the trigonometric functions lose their special character of being associated with angles, and join the rest of mathematics as useful and important functions of numbers. Now that they are defined as functions of a real variable, which hereafter

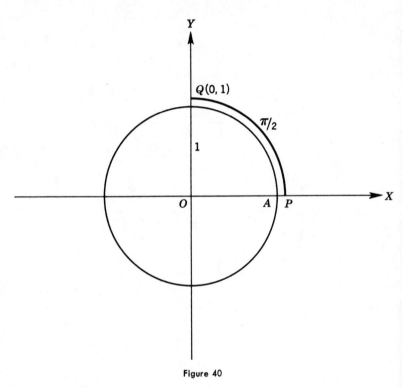

Figure 40

we call x, the modern course proceeds to find their properties. We prove identities such as:

$$\sin^2 x + \cos^2 x = 1,$$
$$\sin 2x = 2 \sin x \cos x.$$

We solve equations such as

$$4 \sin^2 x - 4 \sin x + 1 = 0,$$

and we define the inverse functions such as

$$\text{arc sin } x, \qquad \text{arc cos } x.$$

Applications

This is the theoretical part of the subject which was badly neglected in so many traditional courses. In addition to this we need to include a full range of contemporary applications to physics and engineering. One of the most appealing of these is concerned with

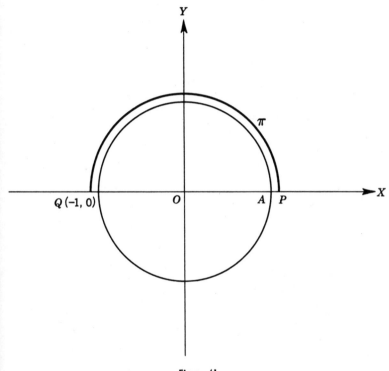

Figure 41

wave motion. The graph of $y = \sin x$ is the basis of this and has the form shown in Fig. 42. This can be modified by inserting coefficients to read

$$y = A \sin Bx.$$

The factor A is called the *amplitude* and controls the height of the maximum and the depth of the minimum of the curve. The factor B is related to the *frequency* of the curve, and tells us how many complete vibrations occur within a fixed horizontal distance. In ordinary house current, the amplitude corresponds to the voltage (usually 110 volts) and the frequency to the number of cycles per second (usually 60). By varying the amplitude continuously, we can

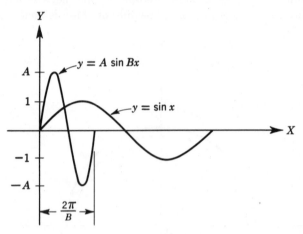

Figure 42

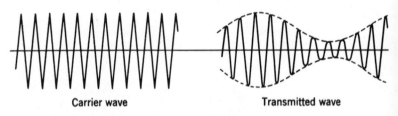

Carrier wave   Transmitted wave

Amplitude Modulation

Figure 43

send a signal on such a wave transmitted by a radio station. This is the basic idea of AM, or amplitude modulation radio. Similarly, by varying the frequency, we can obtain FM or frequency modulation. (Sée Figs. 43 and 44.) These applications are only a few of the ways in which trigonometry is now used in science, and it is very important that we introduce applications such as these into the curriculum in place of the obsolete materials of yesteryear.

Logarithms

Since logarithms are so commonly associated with trigonometry in school courses, I should comment on their place in contemporary mathematics. Originally logarithms were invented to provide a means for carrying out long series of multiplications and divisions. By means of the basic formulas

$$\log xy = \log x + \log y, \qquad \log \frac{x}{y} = \log x - \log y,$$

multiplication was converted into addition, and division into subtraction. This was a major advance, for addition and subtraction

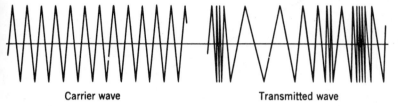

Carrier wave   Transmitted wave

Frequency Modulation

Figure 44

are numerically simpler than multiplication and division. This need for logarithms, however, has entirely disappeared, for modern desk calculators and high-speed computing machines now make arithmetic a trivial and mechanical operation. There is no point whatever in teaching logarithms to present-day students for this purpose.

On the other hand, there are many theoretical and practical aspects of logarithms that make them an essential part of a mathematical education. In the first place there are many physical processes whose law of behavior can be expressed only in terms of logarithms. For example, consider radioactive decay. If one starts with A grams of a radioactive substance, the number of grams, x, remaining after t seconds is given by the formula

$$x = Ae^{-(t \log_e 2)/\tau},$$

where e is an irrational number approximately equal to 2.71828 and τ is the *half-life* of the substance, that is, the time required for A

grams to decay into $A/2$ grams. The graph of this function is given in Fig. 45.

Another use for logarithms occurs in the graphical presentation of percentage change. Suppose that you play the stock market and wish to chart the behavior of your favorite stock. You may well plot the price against time and obtain a graph like that shown in Fig. 46.

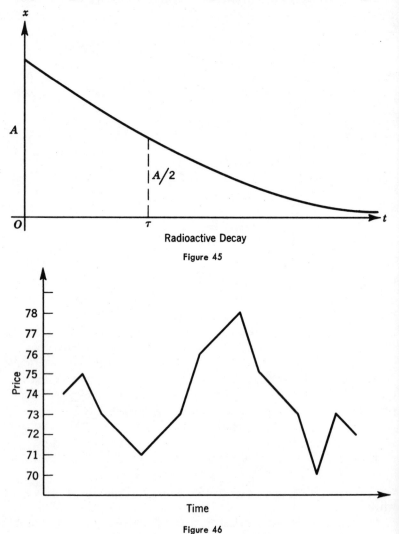

Radioactive Decay

Figure 45

Figure 46

This is satisfactory if you are interested in absolute gains or losses, but many investors place greater importance on percentage gains or losses.

Suppose that on successive days a stock sells at 76 and 81 for an absolute gain of 5. The percentage gain, however, is $5/76 = 0.07 = 7$

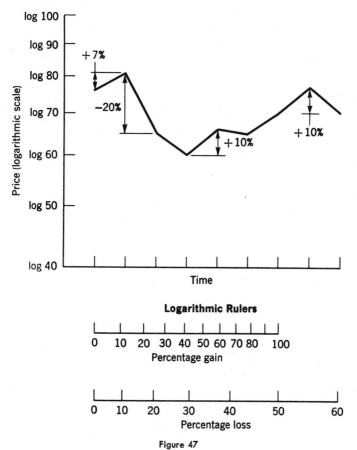

Figure 47

per cent. This involves arithmetic, and you may prefer to do it graphically. The trick is to plot log 76 and log 81 against time instead of plotting 76 and 81. Then the vertical distance

$$\log 81 - \log 76 = \log \frac{81}{76} = \log 1.07.$$

By using a logarithmic vertical scale and a logarithmic ruler, you can read percentage changes directly from the graph. Moreover, a gain of 10 per cent (say) corresponds to the same vertical distance no matter what the base price. Thus percentage changes at different times are easily compared. Since it would be a nuisance to have to look up logarithms in a table for graphs of this type, special paper called "semilog" is available. On this paper the vertical scale is

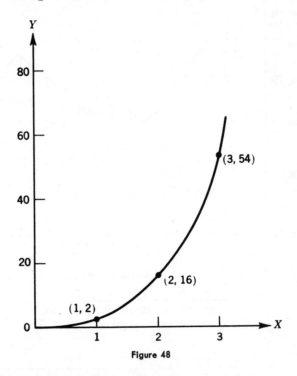

Figure 48

already logarithmic, and the prices can be plotted directly without looking up their logarithms. (See Fig. 47.)

As a final application suppose that you wish to plot the graph of

$$y = 2x^3 \quad \text{for } x \geq 0.$$

This is as shown in Fig. 48. A simpler procedure (and a more accurate one) is to write the given equation as

$$\log y = \log 2 + 3 \log x.$$

Now plot $\log y$ against $\log x$. The result is a straight line. The easiest way to do this is to use "log-log" graph paper on which both the vertical and horizontal scales are logarithmic. (See Fig. 49.)

It is for applications like these that logarithms need to be taught; let us leave computing to the machines.

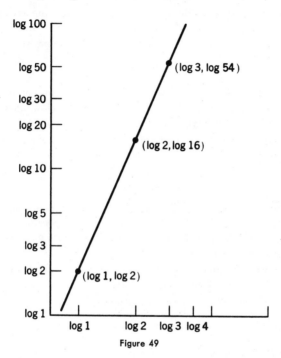

Figure 49

PROBLEMS

1. Using the definitions of the trigonometric functions compute:

(a) $\sin 2\pi$

(b) $\cos 2\pi$

(c) $\sin \dfrac{3\pi}{2}$

(d) $\cos \dfrac{3\pi}{2}$

(e) $\sin 5\pi$

(f) $\cos 5\pi$

(g) $\sin (-\pi)$

(h) $\cos (-\pi)$

(i) $\sin \left(-\dfrac{\pi}{2}\right)$

(j) $\cos \left(-\dfrac{\pi}{2}\right)$

2. Explain what is meant by the numbers on your radio dial.

3. Why is $\sin^2 z + \cos^2 z = 1$?

4. Why is there no solution to the equation $\sin x = 2$?

5. Plot $y = 2^x$ on a conventional set of axes. Then plot $\log_{10} y$ against x. What is the nature of the curves?

6. Suppose that banks finally go the limit and compound savings interest not annually, not quarterly, not weekly, not hourly, but *continuously*. Then an amount of P dollars ar r per cent interest is worth

$$A = Pe^{rt/100}$$

dollars after t years. How much interest at 4 per cent per annum would be paid on a deposit of \$100 during the first year? How much would the first year's interest have been if it had been compounded quarterly?

7. For small values of x, a good approximation to $\sin x$ is

$$\sin x = x - \frac{x^3}{6}.$$

Compute $\sin (0.1)$ to four decimal places, and compare your result with its value in a published table. You will need to consult a table which gives the sine of an angle of 0.1 radians, for published tables have not caught up with the times.

8. From the definition show that $\sin (2\pi + x) = \sin x$. Hence using the result of Prob. 7 compute $\sin 6.38$.

9. Give an example to show that in general

$$\sin (x + y) \neq \sin x + \sin y.$$

Hence a possible extension of the distributive law is false.

10. From the definition show that $\sin (-x) = -\sin x$.

ANSWERS

1. (a) 0.   (f) -1.
   (b) 1.   (g) 0.
   (c) -1.   (h) -1.
   (d) 0.   (i) -1.
   (e) 0.   (j) 0.

2. The number 550 refers to 550 kilocycles. This means that the carrier wave of this station has 550,000 periods per second. A period of a sine wave is that illustrated in Fig. 42.

3. By definition $\sin z = y$, $\cos z = x$, where x and y are the coordinates of the end point of an arc of length z starting at point A in Fig. 38. For any point on a circle of radius one, $x^2 + y^2 = 1$. Hence

$$\sin^2 z + \cos^2 z = 1.$$

4. Sin x lies between -1 and $+1$ inclusive.

5.

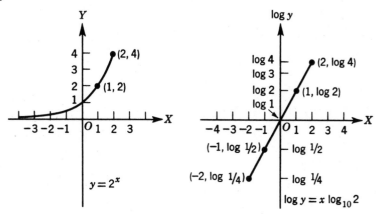

6. Compounded continuously, interest $= \$4.08$. For $e^{0.04} = 1.0408$. Compounded quarterly, interest $= \$4.06$.

7. $\sin(0.1) = 0.1 - \dfrac{0.001}{6}$

$= 0.1 - 0.0002$
$= 0.0998.$

8. An arc of length $2\pi + x$ wraps around the circle completely with x left over. Hence the end point of such an arc is the same as the end point of an arc of length x. *Ans.* 0.0998.

9. Let $x = \dfrac{\pi}{2}$, $y = \dfrac{\pi}{2}$, $x + y = \pi$. Then $\sin x = 1$, $\sin y = 1$, $\sin(x + y) = 0$. $0 \neq 1 + 1$.

10. The end point of the arc corresponding to $(-x)$ is directly below that corresponding to x. Since the figure is symmetrical relative to the X-axis, $\sin(-x) = -\sin x$.

CHAPTER 13 LOGIC

The process of *proof* runs throughout all branches of mathematics and is an essential ingredient of a modern high school course in mathematics. In order to understand a proof a student needs to have an elementary introduction to logic. In the past it has been assumed that an intelligent youngster could learn his logic by seeing how it was used by the teacher and in the textbook, that is, by a process of osmosis. For the very bright student this was, indeed, satisfactory, but for others it is now clear that formal instruction is necessary. This chapter has, therefore, been written as a brief summary of the essentials of logic and the nature of proof.

Sentences and Open Sentences

A sentence is a simple statement which is so clearly expressed that it is meaningful to call it *true* or *false*. Examples of sentences are:

> Boston is in Massachusetts.
> Diamonds are a girl's best friend.

Although mathematics uses sentences to some extent, the most common type of mathematical statement is an *open sentence*. This is a statement which contains a variable and which cannot be said to be true or false unless we specify the value of the variable. Examples of open sentences are:

$$x + 3 = 7. \quad \text{True if } x = 4, \text{ false for other values of } x.$$
$$x^2 + 5x + 4 = 0. \quad \text{True if } x = -1 \text{ or } -4, \text{ false for other values of } x.$$

Some open sentences are true for every value of the variable; these are called *identities*. Examples are

$$x^2 - 4 = (x + 2)(x - 2),$$
$$\sqrt{x^2} = |x|.$$

Similarly, some open sentences are true for no value of the variable. Examples are

$$x^2 = -1, \quad \text{where } x \text{ is to be real};$$
$$0 \times x = 5.$$

Compound Open Sentences

In constructing mathematical arguments, we often combine two or more open sentences containing the same variable into a new, compound, open sentence by the use of connective words such as *and* and *or*. We must then give rules for deciding about the truth of the compound open sentence for a particular value of the variable. Of course, this depends on our previous knowledge of the truth of the component parts for this same value of x. A simple example is

$$x^2 = 4 \quad \text{and} \quad (x - 2)(x - 3) = 0.$$

So that we can analyze this situation, let me introduce some notation to be used later.

Let p_x be the open sentence: $x^2 = 4$;
   q_x be the open sentence: $(x - 2)(x - 3) = 0$;
   $p_x \wedge q_x$ be the open sentence: p_x and q_x.

The symbol $\wedge$ stands for "and," and $p_x \wedge q_x$ is called the *conjunction* of p_x, q_x. Now for what values of x is $p_x \wedge q_x$ true? The answer is based upon a definition which itself is intended to follow common sense.

Definition. $p_x \wedge q_x$ *is true for a particular value of x if both p_x and q_x are true for this value of x. Otherwise $p_x \wedge q_x$ is false for this value of x.*

To illustrate this definition, let me apply it to the example above.

Open Sentence	Values of x for Which the Open Sentence Is	
	True	False
p_x	−2, +2	All x except −2, +2
q_x	2, 3	All x except 2, 3
$p_x \wedge q_x$	2	All x except 2

A standard way of formalizing this definition is a "truth table", such as that below.

CONJUNCTION

p_x	q_x	$p_x \wedge q_x$
T	T	T
T	F	F
F	T	F
F	F	F

In this table T stands for "true" and F for "false". To read the table, choose a value of x and determine whether, for this x, p_x and q_x are individually T or F. Enter the corresponding line of the table and read T or F under $p_x \wedge q_x$.

We can put this another way by considering the corresponding truth sets (see Chapter 6). The truth set of $p_x \wedge q_x$ is then the intersection of the truth sets of p_x and of q_x respectively.

In a similar fashion we may connect two open sentences with the word "or". In mathematics "or" means "either or both" and is used in the sense of the legal phrase "and/or". The symbol $\vee$ stands for "or" and $p_x \vee q_x$ is called the *disjunction* of p_x, q_x. The corresponding truth table is:

DISJUNCTION

p_x	q_x	$p_x \lor q_x$
T	T	T
T	F	T
F	T	T
F	F	F

In terms of truth sets we see that the truth set of $p_x \lor q_x$ is the union of the truth sets of p_x and of q_x respectively.

Equivalent Open Sentences

Two open sentences may have quite different forms of expression, but still have identical truth sets. For example,

$$x^2 + 5x = -6,$$

and

$$(x + 2)(x + 3) = 0.$$

have the same truth sets. This leads us to the definition of *equivalent* open sentences.

Definition. *Two open sentences are equivalent if and only if they have identical truth sets.*

The corresponding truth table is:

EQUIVALENCE

p_x	q_x	$p_x \leftrightarrow q_x$
T	T	T
T	F	F
F	T	F
F	F	T

The symbol $\leftrightarrow$ is read "is equivalent to". Much of ordinary algebra consists of learning how to transform a somewhat complicated open sentence into a simpler one which is equivalent to it.

The Negation of an Open Sentence

Associated with each open sentence is another open sentence called its *negation*. The negation of p_x is written $\sim p_x$. The basic idea behind this is that the truth set of $\sim p_x$ consists of those values of x for which p_x is false. That is, the truth set of $\sim p_x$ is the complement of the truth set of p_x. Often we can form negations by inserting a "not" in an appropriate place. For example:

p_x	$\sim p_x$
$x^2 = 4$	x^2 is not equal to 4; i.e., $x^2 \neq 4$
Triangle x is isosceles	Triangle x is not isosceles

In other cases the formation of negations is more complicated. The corresponding truth table is:

NEGATION

p_x	$\sim p_x$
T	F
F	T

Implication

The great bulk of mathematical theorems are of the form: If p_x, then q_x. For example:

If x is an even number, then $x + 1$ is an odd number.

There is, moreover, a subtlety here that is all too frequently ignored. In our example above, we really mean:

For *all* integers x: If x is an even number, then $x + 1$ is an odd number.

In other words, our theorems are *general* statements which are to be true for *all* values of our variable. We write such an implication in the symbolic form

$$V_x \, (p_x \rightarrow q_x),$$

which is read: "For all x: If p_x, then q_x".

In order to make progress, we must say what is meant by the truth of $p_x \to q_x$ for a particular value of x. To gain some feeling for the situation, let us consider the example:

For all x: If $x^2 = 4$, then $(x - 2)(x - 3) = 0$.

Let p_x be $x^2 = 4$, q_x be $(x - 2)(x - 3) = 0$.

Then we have

Values of x	p_x	q_x	$p_x \to q_x$
2	T	T	
−2	T	F	To be
3	F	T	defined
Any other x	F	F	

The question now is what to write in the right hand column. The answer may seem arbitrary, but it works out quite well. It is given by the truth table:

IMPLICATION

p_x	q_x	$p_x \to q_x$
T	T	T
T	F	F
F	T	T
F	F	T

In our example above we see that $p_x \to q_x$ is true for all values of x except $x = -2$, and that it is false for $x = -2$. Hence it is not true for *all* x, and the statement

For *all* x: If $x^2 = 4$, then $(x - 2)(x - 3) = 0$

is false. Hence this is not a theorem which we are entitled to use in later work.

On the contrary, consider the example

For all x: If $x = 2$, then $x^2 = 4$.

Let p_x be $x = 2$, and let q_x be $x^2 = 4$. We have:

Values of x	p_x	q_x	$p_x \rightarrow q_x$
2	T	T	T
-2	F	T	T
Any other x	F	F	T

In this table there is no entry where p_x is T and q_x is F, and (therefore) $p_x \rightarrow q_x$ is F. Thus our implication *is* true for all values of x. It is, indeed, a useful theorem.

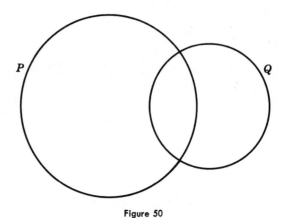

Figure 50

There is one very important point to notice, namely, we really need not bother with those values of x for which p_x is false, for regardless of the truth or falsehood of q_x for these values, $p_x \rightarrow q_x$ is true. We can then concentrate on those values of x for which p_x is true. For every one of these we must show that q_x is true. If there is a single value of x for which p_x is true and q_x is false, then our main statement: $V_x \, (p_x \rightarrow q_x)$ is false.

This situation can be explained in another way by Fig. 50. Let the points of the page in your book represent all possible values of x, that is, the universal set. Let those values of x for which p_x is true lie inside the circle labeled P, and those for which q_x is true lie inside the circle labeled Q. Of the many relative positions in which circles P and Q may lie, there are just two which correspond to the statement that $\mathrm{V}_x\,(p_x \to q_x)$ is true, namely, the situations when P lies inside Q or is identical with Q (Fig. 51).

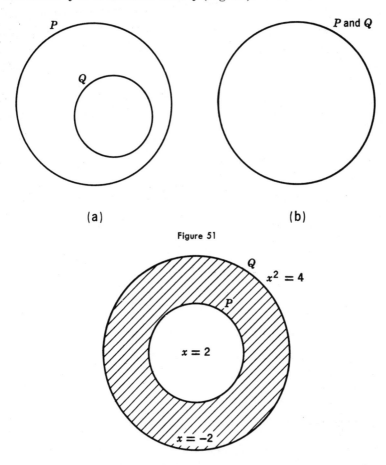

(a)   (b)

Figure 51

Figure 52

In our example

For all x: If $x = 2$, then $x^2 = 4$

the figure looks like Fig. 52. The large circle includes points where $x^2 = 4$, namely, $x = -2$ and $x = 2$. The small circle contains $x = 2$

only. The shaded region corresponds to $x = -2$. Since P lies inside Q, the theorem is true.

In our previous example:

$$\text{For all } x: \text{If } x^2 = 4, \text{ then } (x - 2)(x - 3) = 0$$

Fig. 53 applies. Since P contains points not in Q, the theorem is false.

In summary, to prove a statement of the form $V_x\,(p_x \to q_x)$, we consider all x for which p_x is true. We then check to see whether q_x is

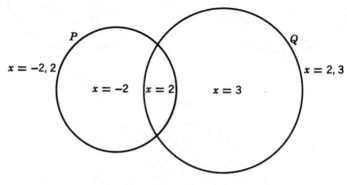

Figure 53

true for all these values of x. If it is, the statement is true. If, however, there is a single x for which p_x is true and q_x is false, the statement is false.

Implications Related to a Given Implication

Associated with the implication $V_x\,(p_x \to q_x)$ there are three other implications with which it is often confused:

Converse: $V_x\,(q_x \to p_x).$
Inverse: $V_x\,(\sim p_x \to \sim q_x).$
Contrapositive: $V_x\,(\sim q_x \to \sim p_x).$

The question is whether any or all of these are equivalent to the given implication. We can settle this in two ways.

First, let us use an extended form of our truth tables.

Line	p_x	q_x	$\sim p_x$	$\sim q_x$	Given, $p_x \to q_x$	Converse, $q_x \to p_x$	Inverse, $\sim p_x \to \sim q_x$	Contra-positive, $\sim q_x \to \sim p_x$
1	T	T	F	F	T	T	T	T
2	T	F	F	T	F	T	T	F
3	F	T	T	F	T	F	F	T
4	F	F	T	T	T	T	T	T

To construct this table we give p_x and q_x all possible combinations of values of T and F in the first two columns. We then write T or F on each line of succeeding columns as we are directed to do by our earlier truth tables for negation and implication.

From this table we see that in the case where $p_x \to q_x$ is true for all values of x (that is, there are no x's corresponding to line 2) there may be x's for which its converse is false (line 3). Similarly, there may be x's for which the converse is true and the given implication is false (line 2). Hence the given implication and its converse may not be equivalent. For example,

$$\text{If } x = 2, \text{ then } x^2 = 4$$

is not equivalent to

$$\text{If } x^2 = 4, \text{ then } x = 2.$$

On the other hand, an implication and its converse may be equivalent. This occurs when there are no x's corresponding to either line 2 or to line 3. For example,

$$\text{If } 3x = 6, \text{ then } x = 2$$

is equivalent to

$$\text{If } x = 2, \text{ then } 3x = 6.$$

In a similar way we can show that:
An implication and its inverse may not be equivalent.
The converse and inverse of an implication are always equivalent.
An implication and its contrapositive are always equivalent.

A second way of seeing this is by means of circular diagrams like those above. Let us consider an implication and its converse (Fig. 54). The given implication states that P is inside Q or is identical with Q, and the converse that Q is inside P or is identical with P. These two statements will be contradictory unless P and Q are identical; hence they are not equivalent. I leave consideration of the inverse and the contrapositive to the problems.

In summary, it is false reasoning to conclude that the converse or the inverse of a true implication is true. It may or may not be

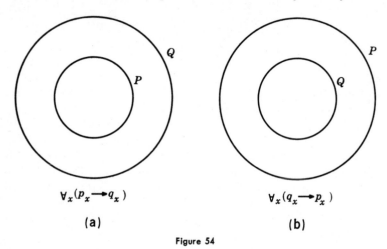

$$\forall_x (p_x \longrightarrow q_x)$$

(a)

$$\forall_x (q_x \longrightarrow p_x)$$

(b)

Figure 54

true, and more investigation is required. It is correct, however, to conclude that the contrapositive of a true implication is true.

Direct Proof

The most common type of mathematical proof is a direct proof involving a chain of implications which have previously been shown to be true. Suppose that we are given that the following are true:

$$\forall_x (p_x \to q_x), \quad \forall_x (q_x \to r_x), \quad \forall_x (r_x \to s_x).$$

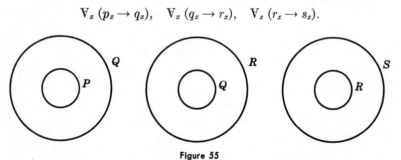

Figure 55

We wish to prove that $V_x\ (p_x \rightarrow s_x)$. The argument is immediate; for we are given the diagrams in Fig. 55. In order to save space we shall draw such diagrams with circle P inside circle Q, but we interpret this to mean that P is either inside Q or identical with Q. From these we derive Fig. 56. Thus P is contained in S and $V_x\ (p_x \rightarrow s_x)$ is true.

There are endless variations of this pattern, and great skill is required in arranging the work so that the proof is valid. One com-

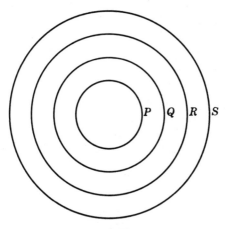

Figure 56

mon trick, for instance, is the replacement of an implication by its contrapositive if this will simplify matters. For example:

Given: $V_x\ (p_x \rightarrow \sim q_x),\ V_x\ (r_x \rightarrow q_x).$

Prove: $V_x\ (p_x \rightarrow \sim r_x).$

Proof: Since $V_x\ (r_x \rightarrow q_x)$ is equivalent to $V_x\ (\sim q_x \rightarrow \sim r_x)$, we have the chain: $V_x\ (p_x \rightarrow \sim q_x),\ V_x\ (\sim q_x \rightarrow \sim r_x).$ Hence we conclude that $V_x\ (p_x \rightarrow \sim r_x)$ is true.

As a specific example, consider the following proof of

For all integers x: If x is odd, then x^2 is odd.

This amounts to the following:

Given: For all x: If x is odd, then $x = 2a + 1$, where a is an integer.
For all x: If $x = 2a + 1$, where a is an integer, then x is odd.
The rules of algebra.

Prove: For all x: If x is odd, then x^2 is odd.

Proof:

1. For all x: If x is odd, then $x = 2a + 1$.   (Given)
2. For all x: If $x = 2a + 1$, then $x^2 = 4a^2 + 4a + 1$.   (Algebra)
3. $4a^2 + 4a + 1 = 2(2a^2 + 2a) + 1 = 2b + 1$,   where b is an integer.   (Algebra)
4. For all x: If $x = 2a + 1$, then $x^2 = 2b + 1$, where b is an integer.   (Substitution)
5. For all x: If $x^2 = 2b + 1$, where b is an integer, then x^2 is odd.
                                                                              (Given)
6. For all x: If x is odd, then x^2 is odd.   (From 1, 4, and 5)

Indirect Proof

This method of proof is a bugbear to students and teachers alike, but it is really very straightforward. The idea is that $V_x (p_x \rightarrow q_x)$ must be either true or false. If we can show that it is not false, then it must be true. We proceed by assuming that it is false, combining this assumption with other known facts, and (with luck) arriving at a contradiction. Since contradictions are impossible in correct thinking, we must have made a mistake somewhere. Our only dubious statement was the assumption that $V_x (p_x \rightarrow q_x)$ is false. Hence this must be in error, and $V_x (p_x \rightarrow q_x)$ must be true.

The difficulty in practice usually arises when a student tries to state that $V_x (p_x \rightarrow q_x)$ is false. But from what we saw above the correct procedure is crystal clear; the only way that $V_x (p_x \rightarrow q_x)$ can be false is that,

For some x, p_x is true and q_x is false.

That is, some point inside the P circle must be outside the Q circle. Let us try an example:

Prove: For all integers x: If x^2 is even, then x is even.

Proof: We assume that the given implication is false, namely, that:

For some x: x^2 is even and x is odd (not even).

From our previous proof, above, however, we know that it is impossible for x to be odd and x^2 to be even. Hence we have arrived at a contradiction; our assumption is incorrect, and the statement to be proved is true.

Disproof

Students sometimes have difficulty in disproving statements which are asserted to be true for *all* x. For example, how do you disprove

$$\text{For all } x: x^2 + 16 = (x - 4)(x + 4).$$

There is a natural procedure: find *one* value of x for which the open sentence is false. Such an x is called a *counterexample*. In the above example $x = 0$ will do the job.

Conclusion

This has been a very brief and informal discussion of logic and methods of proof and disproof, but I hope that you have some idea of these topics. The construction of a proof often involves ingenuity of a high order, and this takes time to develop even if the brain power is adequate. It is nowhere nearly so difficult to recognize a correct proof when you see one, and I hope that this discussion will help you find your way through some of the modern textbooks your children are using.

PROBLEMS

1. Using truth tables show that $(p_x) \lor (\sim p_x)$ is true for all values of x. *Hint:* Fill in the right-hand column of the table:

p_x	$\sim p_x$	$(p_x) \lor (\sim p_x)$
T	F	
F	T	

2. Using truth tables show that $\sim[(p_x) \land (\sim p_x)]$ is true for all values of x.

3. Using truth tables show that $p_x \to q_x$ is equivalent to $\sim[(p_x) \land (\sim q_x)]$.

4. In order to treat the inverse and contrapositive of $V_x (p_x \to q_x)$ in our diagrammatic fashion, we draw a square to represent the universal set consisting of all values of x. The circle P inside this square contains those values of x for which p_x is true. The remainder of the square contains those x for which p_x is false (figure below) that is, for which $(\sim p_x)$ is true. Using this idea show that $V_x \, (p_x \rightarrow q_x)$ and $V_x \, [(\sim q_x) \rightarrow (\sim p_x)]$ are equivalent.

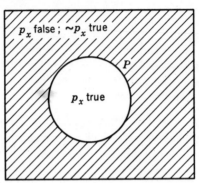

5. As in Prob. 4, by diagrams show that $V_x \, (q_x \rightarrow p_x)$ and $V_x \, [(\sim p_x) \rightarrow (\sim q_x)]$ are equivalent.

6. Construct a proof for the following, or show that no such proof exists.
   Given: For all x: If $x^4 = 16$, then $x^2 = 4$.
            For all x: If $x = 2$, then $x^2 = 4$.
   Prove: For all x: If $x^4 = 16$, then $x = 2$.

7. Construct a proof for the following, or show that no such proof exists.
   Given: For all x: If $x^4 = 16$, then $x^2 = 4$.
            For all x: If x is other than -2, 2, then $x^2 \neq 4$.
   Prove: For all x: If $x^4 = 16$, then $x = -2$ or 2.

8. Give a direct proof of:
   For all integers x: If x is even, then x^2 is even.

9. By means of an indirect proof, establish the truth of: For all integers x: If x^2 is odd, then x is odd.

10. Prove or disprove:
    For all real numbers a, b, c, d: If $a > b$ and $c < d$, then $a + c > b + d$.

11. Is the following a correct indirect proof?
    Prove: For all a, b: If a and b are integers, then $(a/b)^2 \neq 2$.
    Proof:
    (1) Assume that for one pair of integers, a and b, $(a/b)^2 = 2$.
    (2) Let k be the greatest common divisor of a and b so that $a = kp$, $b = kq$, where p and q are integers with no factors in common. Then $(a/b)^2 = (kp/kq)^2 = p^2/q^2 = 2$.
    (3) $p^2 = 2q^2$.
    (4) p^2 is even, so $p = 2r$.

(5) $4r^2 = 2q^2$.

(6) $2r^2 = q^2$.

(7) q^2 is even.

(8) q is even, so $q = 2s$.

(9) p and q have 2 as a common factor.

(10) Step 9 contradicts step 2.

(11) Therefore, the assumption in step 1 is incorrect and the theorem is proved true.

12. Is the following a correct indirect proof?

Prove: For all x: If $x \geq 3$, then $x^2 \geq 9$.

Proof:

(1) Assume: For all x: If $x < 3$, then $x^2 < 9$.

(2) Let $x = -5$. Then $-5 < 3$, but $(-5)^2 = 25$ and is not <9. Thus $x = -5$ is counterexample to step 1, and step 1 is false.

(3) Since the assumption in step 1 is false, the theorem is true.

13. Some theorems in mathematics cannot be written conveniently in the form $V_x (p_x \rightarrow q_x)$, but indirect proof can still be applied to them. Consider the theorem:

There exist an infinite number of primes.

Recall that a prime is a positive integer which has no integral divisors except itself and 1. To prove this theorem we proceed as follows:

(1) Assume that the theorem is false, that is, assume that: There are only n prime numbers, where n is a (finite) positive integer.

(2) Then we can make a list of these primes, say, $p_1, p_2, \ldots, p_n$.

(3) Consider $P = p_1 \times p_2 \times \cdots \times p_n + 1$. We wish to produce a contradiction by showing that P is a prime not in the above list of *all* primes.

(4) First, P is not equal to any of $p_1, \ldots, p_n$, for it is clearly larger than any of them.

(5) Second, P is a prime (prove it).

(6) Hence there is a contradiction with our assumption in step 1 and the theorem is true.

ANSWERS

1.

p_x	$\sim p_x$	$(p_x) \vee (\sim p_x)$
T	F	T
F	T	T

2.

p_x	$\sim p_x$	$(p_x) \wedge (\sim p_x)$	$\sim[(p_x) \wedge (\sim p_x)]$
T	F	F	T
F	T	F	T

3.

p_x	q_x	$\sim q_x$	$(p_x) \wedge (\sim q_x)$	$\sim[(p_x) \wedge (\sim q_x)]$	$(p_x \rightarrow q_x)$
T	T	F	F	T	T
T	F	T	T	F	F
F	T	F	F	T	T
F	F	T	F	T	T

The two open sentences are equivalent since the pattern of T's and F's in the last two columns is the same.

4. Assume $V_x (p_x \rightarrow q_x)$ is true. Then we have the diagrams below. Hence

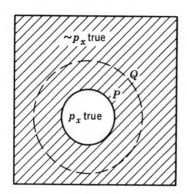
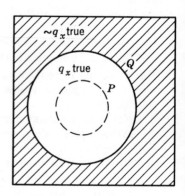

the region where $\sim q_x$ is true is included in the region where $\sim p_x$ is true, or $V_x [(\sim q_x) \rightarrow (\sim p_x)]$ is true. Now reverse the process to complete the argument.

5. Assume $V_x (q_x \rightarrow p_x)$ is true. Then we have the diagrams:

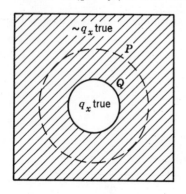
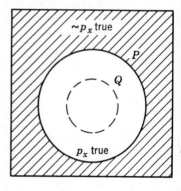

Hence the region where $\sim p_x$ is true is included in the region where $\sim q_x$ is true, or $V_x[(\sim p_x) \to (\sim q_x)]$ is true. Now reverse the process.

6. There can be no proof, for $x = -2$ is a counterexample to the conclusion.

7. Proof:
 (1) For all x: If $x^4 = 16$, then $x^2 = 4$.   (Given)
 (2) For all x: If x is other than $x = -2, 2$, then $x^2 \neq 4$.   (Given)
 (3) For all x: If $x^2 = 4$, then $x = -2$ or 2. (Contrapositive of step 2)
 (4) For all x: If $x^4 = 16$, then $x = -2$ or 2.   (From steps 1 and 3)

8. Proof:
 (1) For all x: If x is even, then $x = 2a$ where a is an integer. (Given)
 (2) For all x: If $x = 2a$, then $x^2 = 4a^2$.   (Algebra)
 (3) $4a^2 = 2(2a^2) = 2b$, where b is an integer.   (Algebra)
 (4) For all x: If $x = 2a$, then $x^2 = 2b$, where b is an integer.
                     (Substitution)
 (5) For all x: If $x^2 = 2b$, where b is an integer, then x^2 is even. (Given)
 (6) For all x: If x is even, then x^2 is even.   (From steps 1, 4, and 5)

9. Proof:
 (1) Assume that, for some x, x^2 is odd and x is even.
 (2) This contradicts the result of Prob. 8.
 (3) Hence the assumption is incorrect and the theorem is true.

10. False. Let $a = 2$, $b = 1$, $c = 3$, $d = 10$. Then $a > b$ and $c < d$. But $a + c = 5$ and $b + d = 11$. Hence it is false that $a + c > b + d$.

11. This is correct. It shows that there is no rational number a/b whose square is 2, or that $\sqrt{2}$ is irrational.

12. This is incorrect. The assumption in step 1 is the wrong one if you wish to assert that the theorem is false. Actually the implication in step 1 is the inverse of the given implication, which has nothing to do with the case! The correct assumption to make is: For some x: $x \geq 3$ and $x^2 < 9$. This does not lead to any reasonably evident contradiction, and so the method of indirect proof is not suitable for this theorem.

 We can give a simple direct proof as follows: Consider $x^2 - 9$. We know that $x^2 - 9 = (x + 3)(x - 3)$. Now $x \geq 3$; so $x + 3 > 0$ and $(x - 3) \geq 0$. Hence $(x + 3)(x - 3) \geq 0$, or $x^2 \geq 9$.

13. To prove that P is a prime, we use indirect proof again. Assume that P is not a prime. Then P must be divisible by at least one of the existing primes, $p_1, \ldots, p_n$. Since $P = p_1 \times p_2 \times \cdots \times p_n + 1$, this is a contradiction. Hence P is a prime.

CONCLUSION

If you have followed me this far, you should have an understanding of the general trends of the *Revolution in Mathematics*. I have left many things aside such as the introduction of probability, matrix algebra, and calculus into the high school. I have failed to mention by name the host of college and school mathematicians who have contributed their time and energy. I have necessarily slid over many delicate points of mathematics.

I hope, however, that I have given you the flavor of the movement. If you wish to go farther, you should sit down and work through some of the modern textbooks which seem so hard to the teachers, but which are so easy for your children.

INDEX